P9-AFK-578

COLLEGE ARITHMETIC

COLLEGE ARITHMETIC

π

NEW YORK · JOHN WILEY & SONS, INC.
LONDON · CHAPMAN & HALL, LIMITED

W. I. LAYTON

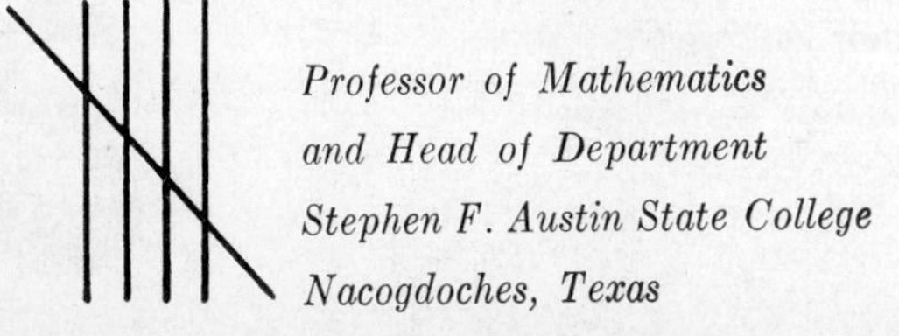

Professor of Mathematics
and Head of Department
Stephen F. Austin State College
Nacogdoches, Texas

Library of Congress Catalog Card Number: 59-14123

Printed in the United States of America

TO MY DAUGHTER, MARY ELIZABETH

PREFACE

College Arithmetic is intended primarily for students entering college without the mathematical understanding and skills necessary for adequate handling of the quantitative problems that arise in everyday affairs. This book may also be used advantageously in connection with adult programs of education.

The text is largely a review of arithmetic, but topics from algebra, commercial arithmetic, and geometry are also presented. My objective has been to offer careful explanations, clear illustrations, and a great abundance of problem material. The problem sets are carefully graded, with the varying abilities of the students taken into account. Answers to the odd-numbered problems are included in the textbook, and answers to the even-numbered problems are available in a separate pamphlet.

For the most part, teachers using this book will probably wish to consider the topics in the order in which they appear. Some teachers may prefer, however, to follow Chapter

Four, "Decimals," with Chapter Seven, "Approximate Numbers."

In *College Arithmetic* I have attempted to present elementary mathematics in such a way that, although little mathematical background is required by the student, he is aware of being treated as a mature individual. It is my sincere hope that the student may become more enthusiastic about mathematics after having worked with this book.

I am deeply indebted to my wife for her patience, understanding, and valuable stenographic assistance in this project.

W. I. Layton

April 1, 1959
Nacogdoches, Texas

CONTENTS

1 — INTRODUCTION 1

2 — WHOLE NUMBERS 5

3 — FRACTIONS 29

4 — DECIMALS 55

5 — WEIGHTS AND MEASURES 71

6 — PERCENTAGE 97

7 — APPROXIMATE NUMBERS 113

8 — ELEMENTARY ALGEBRA 131

9 — AREAS AND VOLUMES OF ELEMENTARY SOLIDS 167

INDEX 197

COLLEGE ARITHMETIC

CHAPTER ONE

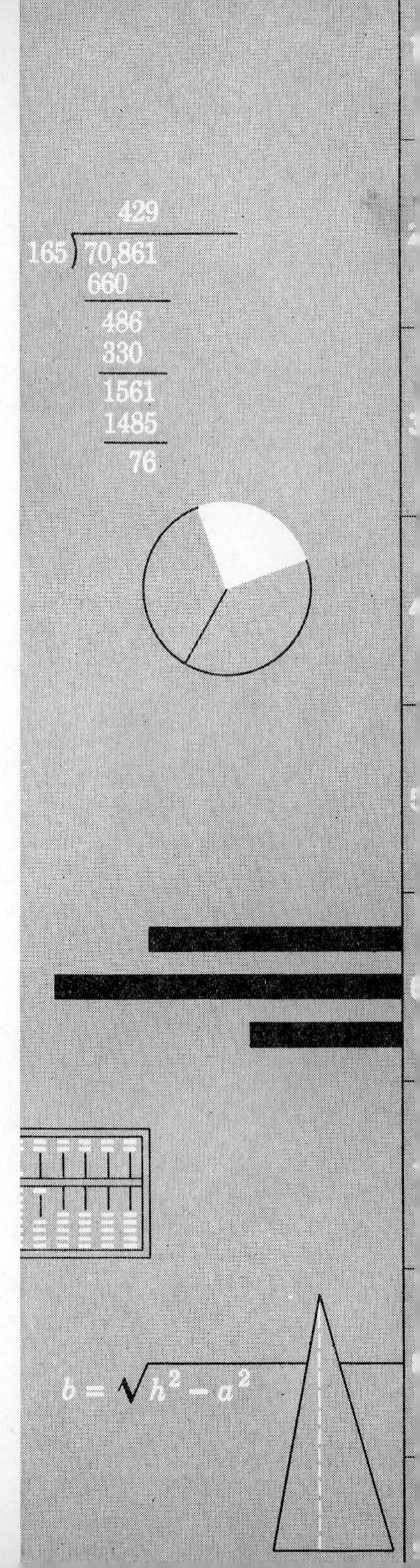

INTRODUCTION

1. WHY STUDY MATHEMATICS?

You will approach the study of *College Arithmetic* with mixed feelings. Very probably some of you have always liked mathematics but have been away from an active study of it for a number of years. Others of you may have felt that mathematics is simply "not for me." In either case, this textbook is intended to be a reorientation for you as far as the basic ideas of mathematics are concerned. It would be well to keep in mind that you should become more skilled in the handling of the elementary mathematics which educated adults frequently use.

Let us consider briefly the impact of mathematics on past and present civilizations. Mathematics had its beginning in prehistoric times. Lancelot Hogben says, "The history of mathematics is the mirror of civilization." *

Many different countries have contributed to mathematics during its centuries of growth, and it has been a common heritage for much of mankind. Today, throughout the civilized world it is regarded as an absolute necessity for further progress.

Although much of mathematics is now highly refined, we are sure that its origin had to do with the everyday matters of food,

* Lancelot Hogben, *Mathematics for the Million,* W. W. Norton and Company, New York, p. 32, 1937.

clothing, and shelter. The basic questions, how much? how many? how long? could be answered only by counting and measuring. These processes under incessant pounding from hunger, cold, and desire gave the basic incentive for the creation of mathematics, and today, in spite of its tremendous growth, number and form remain among the fundamentals of the subject.

2. HOW TO STUDY MATHEMATICS

Success in the study of mathematics, like success in the study of other subjects in college, comes as a result of enthusiastic application on the part of teacher and student. Keep an open-minded attitude and resolve to succeed in your study of mathematics. Go through each explanation in the textbook carefully with pencil and paper handy in order that you may pry into any steps you do not understand. Ask questions freely and remember that, although mathematics is not easy, it is not a subject that should be studied only by those who are the most highly gifted mentally. Intellectual curiosity and persistence are perhaps the main prerequisites for success. Make it a point not to leave a problem or an idea unless you really understand it.

3. A GLANCE AT WHAT LIES AHEAD

In this book we shall cover the following topics. First, we shall review the fundamental operations of addition, subtraction, multiplication, and division with whole numbers. We shall apply these operations in solving problems. We shall introduce ways of checking our work in these operations, and shall also begin to look into the nature of our number system. Second, we shall take up fractions, and follow this topic with decimals and their applications in business problems and technical work. We shall turn to denominate numbers—the numbers we use in measuring quantities. We shall take up exponents and powers, which are very important in writing numbers as we use them in science and technology. Then we shall consider percentage and approximate numbers. After reviewing these fundamentals we shall do some work with elementary algebra, which is largely a generalization of principles in arithmetic, and we shall finish with some work in the geometry of measuring lengths, areas, and volumes.

Throughout the book we shall try to emphasize the review of

elementary principles sufficiently to refresh your memory in the facts and ideas of arithmetic. We want to provide enough practice to enable you to master the ideas. Many of the problems solved will be those met in everyday affairs in business, civil service work, consumer budgeting, and the basic phases of planning and management. We hope to give you sufficient familiarity with the fundamentals of arithmetic to enable you to carry on successfully with further work in mathematics.

It is a long way from the arithmetic of the multiplication tables to the mathematics of space flight, but the principles of the multiplication table still underlie a great deal of the work done in computing satellite orbits. The first step in the direction of understanding and handling the mathematics of satellite orbits is a sound knowledge of elementary arithmetic. Beyond this step the training progresses through algebra, geometry, trigonometry, analytic geometry, calculus, differential equations, and other branches of mathematics. The experience common to those persons who have made the ascent is that the view from the upper levels is well worth the climb.

Those students who would like to study some of the ideas in higher mathematics and modern mathematics from an elementary point of view will find the following books interesting. Only a knowledge of arithmetic and an interest in numbers are prerequisite to the study of these books.

---

1. Bell, E. T., *Development of Mathematics,* New York, Simon and Schuster, Second Edition, 1945.
2. Bell, E. T., *Men of Mathematics,* New York, Simon and Schuster, 1937.
3. Dantzig, Tobias, *Number: The Language of Science,* New York, The Macmillan Company, Fourth Edition, 1954.
4. Kasner, E., and J. R. Newman, *Mathematics and the Imagination,* New York, Simon and Schuster, 1940.
5. Newman, James R., *The World of Mathematics,* Four Volumes, New York, Simon and Schuster, 1956.

CHAPTER TWO

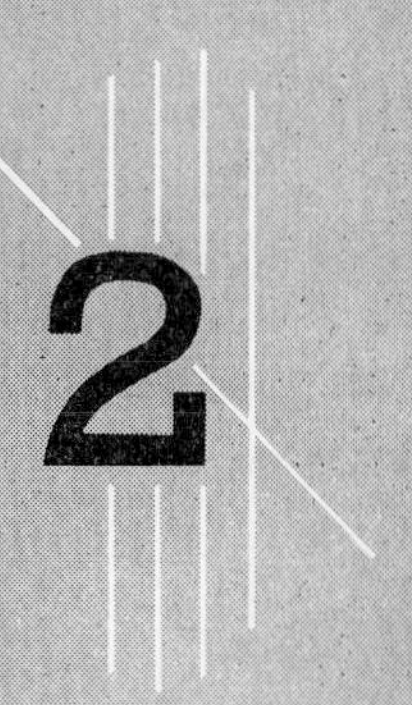

WHOLE NUMBERS

1. INTRODUCTION

The numbers 1, 2, 3, 4, 5, 6, . . . are called the *natural numbers* because it is usually recognized that they have in some philosophical sense a natural existence independent of man. The most complicated of the number systems, on the other hand, are regarded as inventions of the mind of man. This infinite set of numbers has been represented in different ways in the course of history, another rather commonly known representation being the system of Roman numerals I, II, III, IV, V, VI, etc., which we shall discuss in this chapter. The most common representation, 1, 2, 3, . . . , is more often called the Hindu-Arabic or Indo-Arabic system because of the invention of this notation in India. Knowledge of this way of writing numbers was transmitted from India to the Western world by the Arabs. The natural numbers 1, 2, 3, 4, 5, 6 . . . are also known as whole numbers, or integers.

The notation for the natural numbers, 1, 2, 3, 4, 5, 6, 7, 8, 9, 10, 11, 12, 13, 14, . . . , is called the *decimal system* (from the Latin *decem,* meaning ten) because ten symbols or digits are used to represent all numbers. This excellent system of notation is very compact since it is a place or positional system. Thus, in such a number as 632, the digit 6 represents 6 hundreds; the digit

3, 3 tens; the digit 2, 2 units. By comparison, the Roman numeral XXX for 30 has three symbols X of equal value, ten. Let us notice that the Hindu-Arabic system can be used to represent numbers of any size with ten symbols, whereas a non-positional notation such as the Romans used would require new symbols for reasonable brevity in the writing of much larger numbers.

The decimal system is said to have the *base ten.* This system probably originated from the fact that we have ten fingers for use in counting. Ten, however, is not the only possible base. We can use *any natural number greater than one.* In a later portion of this book we shall go into some discussion of the use of two as a base. We shall also elaborate on the meaning of ten as a base.

2. READING AND WRITING WHOLE NUMBERS

It is quite important that we be able to read and write whole numbers. It is convenient to group the digits of a number and to separate these groups by commas. By digits we mean any of the integers 0, 1, 2, 3, 4, 5, 6, 7, 8, 9 appearing in a number. The number 362, for example, has the digits 3, 6, and 2. This number is read three hundred sixty-two, rather than three hundred and sixty-two as we perhaps might commonly read it. The use of *and* in three hundred and sixty-two is approved by the best authorities on English grammar, and its restriction which we have just referred to is purely a mathematical convention. In reading 5647, for instance, we would say five thousand six hundred forty-seven rather than five thousand, six hundred and forty-seven.

Other practices recommended in mathematics in reading and writing numbers are: Only the compound words from twenty-one to ninety-nine are hyphenated. For example, 48 should be written forty-eight. The number 564,897,398,736,416 is described as

564,	897,	398,	736,	416
trillion	billion	million	thousand	units

This number is read five hundred sixty-four trillion, eight hundred ninety-seven billion, three hundred ninety-eight million, seven hundred thirty-six thousand, four hundred sixteen. It should also be noted that the words thousand, million, billion, etc., are written in the singular form. To read larger numbers than the one above requires a knowledge of words beyond trillion.

EXERCISE 1

Write the following numbers in words.

1. 53
2. 68
3. 834
4. 673
5. 9452
6. 3827
7. 24,318
8. 57,632
9. 932,685
10. 873,492
11. 2,521,437
12. 5,847,329
13. 21,524,751
14. 62,378,226
15. 765,725,843
16. 837,429,462
17. 25,764,950,038,847
18. 498,864,578,654,002
19. 37,683,821,062
20. 758,429,253,843

Write the following as numbers.

21. Eight hundred thirty-seven
22. Six hundred twenty-nine
23. Two hundred forty-five thousand nine hundred fifty-eight
24. Twenty-five million, nine hundred twenty-nine thousand, sixty-two
25. Ninety-three trillion, two hundred forty-eight billion, five million, thirty-five thousand, four hundred twenty-seven
26. Six hundred seventy-five billion, forty-three million, three hundred sixty-seven
27. Four hundred eighty-seven billion, two hundred twenty-one million, ninety-three thousand, six
28. Seventy-seven trillion, thirty-nine billion, sixteen million, two thousand, eight hundred twenty-four
29. One trillion, one billion, one million, one thousand, one hundred
30. Eighty-seven billion, twenty-nine thousand, sixty-two

3. ADDING AND SUBTRACTING WHOLE NUMBERS

In adding and subtracting whole numbers, as in the other phases of mathematics we shall come to, we need to concentrate in particular on accuracy and speed. Another point to bear in mind is that we can add and subtract only numbers that are expressed in the same kind of unit. Thus we may add 16 tons and 23 tons, but we cannot add 25 tons and 18 quarts.

Addition is the process of finding the total number of items of a given kind in several sets of items of the same kind. In other words, 5 nickels and 2 quarters are equivalent to 1 quarter and 2 quarters, and their sum is 3 quarters. Also, if we are considering dimes and half dollars, 1 half dollar is equivalent to 50 cents and 1 dime is equal to 10 cents. Then upon adding 8 dimes and 3 half dollars, we obtain 80 cents plus 150 cents = 230 cents.

We use place value in our number system. This means that *10 units* are equal to *1 ten, 10 tens* are equal to *1 hundred, 10 hundreds* are equal to *1 thousand,* and so on. When we have totaled 10 in adding the items in one column, this is equivalent to 1 in the column to its left. We speak of *carrying 10* from one column to obtain *1* in the next column to the left.

For example add:

$$\begin{array}{r} 36 \\ 5679 \\ 247 \\ \hline 5962 \end{array}$$

The numbers to be added, 36, 5679, and 247, are called *addends.* The result of the addition, 5962, in the foregoing example, is called the *sum.*

In this example we notice that the numbers 6, 9, and 7, which are in the units place, are in one column. The numbers 3, 7, and 4, which are in the tens place, are in one column. The numbers 6 and 2, which are in the thousands place, are in one column, etc. It is wise to keep these columns in clean-cut straight lines, as this organization helps to encourage accuracy.

We have pointed out in a recent paragraph that we can add and subtract only numbers that are expressed in the same kind of unit. It does not seem unreasonable therefore that units must be added to units, tens to tens, hundreds to hundreds, etc.

Subtraction is the process of finding the difference between the number of items of a given kind contained in one set, and the number of items of the same kind in a second set. The *difference* or *answer* in subtraction may also be considered as the number of items which *remain* in one set after a number of these items are removed from it.

Subtraction is the *inverse* of *addition.* By this statement we mean that if we add a number and then subtract the same number, the result is the original number. Thus:

$$18 + 5 = 23 \text{ and } 23 - 5 = 18$$

Place value is also important in subtraction. We refer to *borrowing* one item from one column and converting it to ten items in the column to its right. In subtracting, of course, units are subtracted from units, tens from tens, hundreds from hundreds, etc.

In subtracting we also observe a careful lining up of the columns. Thus in subtracting 25,642 from 95,429 we have

95,429
25,642
69,787

In this example, 95,429 is called the *minuend;* 25,642 the *subtrahend;* and 69,787 the *difference* or *remainder.* Thus the number we are subtracting from is called the minuend, the number we are subtracting is called the subtrahend, and the result of the subtraction is known as the difference or remainder. Another way to look at the example is to say that, when we subtract 25,642 from 95,429, we have 25,642 items in one set to be subtracted from 95,429 items of the same kind in another set. The *difference* or *answer,* 69,787, is the number of items which remain in the set that contained 95,429 items, after a set that contains 25,642 items is removed or subtracted. The process of subtraction may be explained by the *decomposition* method or by the *equal additions* method.

We illustrate the *decomposition* method as follows.

Subtract 674 from 935.

hundreds	tens	units
8	1	
~~9~~	3	5
6	7	4
2	6	1

In the units column: 4 from 5 = 1. Write 1 in the units place in the remainder.

In the tens column we cannot take 7 from 3, so we change, or decompose, the 9 hundreds in the minuend into 8 hundreds plus 1 hundred. This 1 hundred is now changed to 10 tens (sometimes this is referred to as "borrowing") and added to the already present 3 tens, making 13 tens in all. It is now possible to subtract the 7 tens of the subtrahend from the 13 tens of the minuend. This leaves 6 tens. Write 6 in the tens place in the remainder.

In the hundreds column, 6 from 8 = 2. We write 2 in the hundreds place in the remainder.

Let us now examine the *equal additions method.*

hundreds	tens	units
	1	
9	3	5
7		
~~6~~	7	4
2	6	1

In the units column, 4 from 5 = 1. Write 1 in the units place in the remainder.

In the tens column we cannot take 7 from 3. We now add 1 hundred to both the minuend and the subtrahend. We see that when we add the same quantity to both minuend and subtrahend, we do not change the remainder. The 1 hundred is added to the minuend as 10 tens, giving 13 tens in all, and added to the subtrahend as 1 hundred, giving 7 hundreds in all. Now we can subtract the 7 tens in the subtrahend from the 13 tens in the minuend. This gives 6 tens. Write 6 in the tens place in the remainder.

In the hundreds column, 7 from 9 = 2. Write 2 in the hundreds place in the remainder.

The *addition check* is the basis for the most frequent check for subtraction. This check is based on the fact that the *remainder* of a subtraction can be thought of as a missing *addend.*

In checking subtraction by addition, add the remainder to the subtrahend. Now see if this sum equals the minuend of the problem.

Check the subtraction 984 − 438 = 546 by addition.

Adding the remainder to the subtraction, we have

```
546
438
---
984
```

Compare the sum 984 just obtained with the minuend 984 of the original problem.

EXERCISE 2

Add in each of the following.

```
1.  2634          2.  25,432
    9871               6,129
    6732              43,817
    4569              71,518
    3127              84,217
    ----              ------
```

3. Add each column, first adding downward, second adding upward to check.

```
23   15   85   38   60   92
48   82   79   47   16   28
16   41   22   75   38   74
71   63   28   40   99   37
43   77   39   22   86   47
55   20   41   44   35   50
81   15   67   61   59   98
60   33   59   87   27   81
--   --   --   --   --   --
```

4. Add each column downward, then add upward to check.

```
385   862   182   703
206    94   238   666
777   603   567   812
581   515   105   284
293    74   903   354
664   567   983   206
---   ---   ---   ---
```

5. Add downward; check by adding upward.

$283.75	$122.46
23.05	321.78
666.30	86.52
500.80	419.00
642.25	73.45
85.50	880.50

6. Add downward; check by adding upward.

$432.75	$4273.80
643.05	6105.60
28.95	1123.40
321.50	695.50
645.90	7820.00
423.35	3000.70

7. Add each set of numbers horizontally, without rewriting, and reading from left to right.

28 + 75 + 93 + 18 + 62 + 44 + 37 + 49 + 66 =
68 + 44 + 19 + 91 + 32 + 73 + 58 + 67 + 21 =
11 + 45 + 63 + 90 + 83 + 47 + 38 + 59 + 62 =
31 + 50 + 64 + 18 + 27 + 65 + 58 + 95 + 17 =
$23.50 + $16.75 + $19.50 + $37.25 + $86.75 = $
$14.72 + $38.71 + $25.63 + $95.52 + $32.45 = $

Check each problem by adding horizontally from right to left.

Add the following:

8.	9.
238	6,742
98,421	839,621
26	23,456
405,782	9,999,999
637	65,431
89,943	278,632
748,632	94,897
9,884,396	38,642,388
21,672,549	38
20,909	256,787

10.
43,821
627,239
46,877
939,342
83,247,883
1,687,889,342
47,662
436,254,889
824,553
4,639,438

Subtract in each of the following, and check by means of the *addition check.*

11. 8374
299

12. 38,573
26,444

13. 624,827
539,449

14. 6,724,329
955,888

15. 8,926,221
3,493,666

16. 6007
4092

17. 91,004
8,903

18. 234,625,500,003
91,016,207,999

19. 63,829,200,004
9,072,998,789

20. 892,437,621,001
29,742,439,909

21. How many pennies would there be in a collection equivalent to the following? 3 quarters, 5 dimes, 4 nickels, and 10 pennies.

How many nickles would there be in a collection having the same value?

22. Tom has 1 quarter, 4 nickels, and 7 pennies. John has 2 quarters and 1 nickel. Which one has more money, and how much more does he have?

23. Mayor Johnson received 3024 votes, and Mr. James received 2368 votes. How many more votes did Mayor Johnson receive?

24. How many quarter inches are there in all of the measurements: $\frac{3}{4}$, $\frac{1}{2}$, $\frac{5}{8}$, $\frac{12}{16}$, $2\frac{1}{2}$, 1, and $\frac{1}{4}$ inches?

25. How many hours will a program last if there are portions taking one-quarter hour, 8 minutes, 12 minutes, 5 minutes, 10 minutes, one-half hour?

26. John has saved $38.23. He wants to buy a suit selling for $52.00. How much does he need?

27. Mr. Smith deposited the following amounts in his bank account during a 3-month period: $25.85, $102.00, $27.75, $43.82, and $63.00. He wrote checks for the following amounts: $21.63, $52.50, $52.50, $48.00, $52.50, and $105.20. If his original balance was $242.83, what was his balance at the end of the 3 months?

28. The goal in a fund raising drive is $36,250. If funds in amount of $27,654.50 have been raised, how much more is needed to reach the goal?

29. Pieces of baggage on a plane weighed 26 pounds, 38 pounds, 49 pounds, 52 pounds, 24 pounds, 44 pounds, and 27 pounds. What was the total weight of baggage?

30. On a trip a family drove distances of 342 miles, 430 miles, 295 miles, 508 miles, and 420 miles. They spent $21.52, $27.25, $32.00, $22.40, and $25.80. How far did they go, and how much did they spend?

4. CHECKING BY CASTING OUT NINES

We shall now describe a check which can be used on all four of the fundamental operations in arithmetic. This check is called the check by "Casting Out Nines." It depends on certain properties of our number system and consists in obtaining a single digit as a representative for each entry in a given problem. This representative is actually a remainder that would be obtained by dividing the given entry by the number nine (9). However, we do not have to divide to get the remainder.

The *remainder* after division of a number by 9 is called the excess. Thus when 20 is divided by 9, the excess is 2. When 35 is divided by 9, the excess is 8.

The *excess* of a number is the same as the *excess* of the sum of the digits of the number. For example, the *excess* of 29 is 2. Adding 2 and 9 we obtain 11 and dividing 11 by 9 we have a remainder of 2 or we may add 1 and 1 in 11 and obtain 2. As another example find the *excess* of 132. Here the *excess* is 6, which we determine by adding $1 + 3 + 2$, the digits in the number. A longer approach would be to divide 132 by 9. This gives 14 and a remainder of 6.

Consider the following example:

Add:

$$\begin{array}{ll} \text{addends}\begin{cases} 384 \to 300 + 80 + 4 \to 3 + 8 + 4 \to 15 \to & 6 \\ 286 \to 200 + 80 + 6 \to 2 + 8 + 6 \to 16 \to & 7 \\ 905 \to 900 + 0 + 5 \to 9 + 0 + 5 \to 14 \to & 5 \\ 371 \to 300 + 70 + 1 \to 3 + 7 + 1 \to 11 \to & 2 \\ 229 \to 200 + 20 + 9 \to 2 + 2 + 9 \to 13 \to & 4 \quad \downarrow \end{cases} & \\ & \overline{} \\ \text{Sum} \qquad 2175 \to 2 + 1 + 7 + 5 \to 15 \to 6 \leftrightarrow & 24 \end{array}$$

The numbers to the right of the addends show the entries split according to place value, and then the remainders for each of these parts are shown after being divided by nine. For example, 300 contributes a remainder 3 because each 100 contributes 1. That is, 100 is 99 + 1 and contains 11 nines plus 1. This remainder fact is true of any power of ten, for example 1,000,000 is 999,999 + 1, hence it contains a collection of nines and a remainder of 1. Again, 80 will contribute 8 as a remainder because each of 8 tens contributes 1 as its remainder.

If we add 3 + 8 + 4 we obtain what is left over after dividing 384 by 9, which is 15, but there is still a 9 in 15. If 9 is removed from 15, 6 will remain, and 6 is the final remainder. Of course we can get 6 by subtracting 9 from 15, but observe also that 10 gives a remainder of 1, and 5 added to 1 gives 6, hence we can get the 6 by adding the 1 and the 5. Try this on 16 and on 24; 9 from 16 leaves 7, but adding the digits in 16, 1 plus 6 also gives 7; twice 9 or 18 from 24 leaves 6, but 2 plus 4 also gives 6.

The check of our problem can now be streamlined as follows.

Add:

$$\begin{array}{rl} 384 \to & 6 \\ 286 \to & 7 \\ 905 \to & 5 \\ 371 \to & 2 \\ 229 \to & 4 \quad \downarrow \\ \hline 2175 \to & 6 \end{array}$$

Notice that any 9 or any combination giving 9 can be dropped immediately. Thus 905 → 0 + 5 since 9 divides 900 evenly. Similarly 229 → 4 + 0 or 4.

In the *sum*, 2 and 7 may be dropped since they total 9; 1 and 5 then give 6 as the representative of the sum. In adding the *representatives,* drop the 7 and 2, which total 9, and the 5 and 4, which total 9, and keep the first 6 as a sum of the representatives. The fact that the final representative, 6, is the same in each case constitutes our check.

Several other examples follow. In each example, the operation used must be applied in the check with the representatives. Thus every check is a skeleton problem paralleling the original, in which entries are replaced by their single-digit representatives.

$$\begin{array}{lrl} \text{Subtract:} & 3861 & \rightarrow 18 \rightarrow 9 \rightarrow 0 \\ & -2903 & \rightarrow 14 \rightarrow 5 \\ \hline & 958 & \rightarrow 13 \rightarrow 4 \end{array}$$

Notice that in the minuend, 3861, we retain a *9* as the representative, in order to be able to subtract 5. It is sometimes necessary to put in extra 9's with the representatives. Such modified representatives are still correct since they are still true remainders that could be obtained on dividing by 9. We can say, for example, that 9 divides 65 six times with a remainder of 11, or that 9 divides 65 seven times with a remainder of 2. Both 11 and 2 are remainders, but 2 is the smallest positive remainder that we can obtain.

EXERCISE 3

1–10. Check the first ten examples in Exercise 2 by casting out nines.

11–20. Check the second ten examples in Exercise 2, that is, numbers 11–20 by casting out nines.

5. MULTIPLYING WHOLE NUMBERS

Multiplication is a process of finding the total of a number of equal sets. Thus the cost of 8 three-cent stamps is equivalent to 8×3 cents or 24 cents. The amount of pay received for 40 hours of work at \$4.00 per hour is $40 \times$ (\$4.00), or \$160.00. Multiplication is a short way of working out an addition problem in which a number of sets of items are added, each set having the same number of items. For example:

$$5 \times (14¢) = 14¢ + 14¢ + 14¢ + 14¢ + 14¢ = 70¢$$

Place value should be understood in multiplication. Thus:

$$\begin{array}{r} 342 \\ \times\ 63 \\ \hline \end{array} \quad \text{is equal to} \quad \begin{array}{r} 342 \\ \times\ (60 + 3) \\ \hline \end{array}$$

or

$$\begin{array}{r} 342 \\ \times\ 60 \\ \hline \end{array} + \begin{array}{r} 342 \\ \times\ 3 \\ \hline \end{array} \quad \text{is equal to} \quad \begin{array}{r} 342 \\ \times\ 60 \\ \hline 20{,}520 \end{array} + \begin{array}{r} 342 \\ \times\ 3 \\ \hline 1026 \end{array} \quad \text{equals}$$

$$\begin{array}{r} 342 \\ \times\ 63 \\ \hline 1026 \\ 2052 \\ \hline 21{,}546 \end{array}$$

In multiplying whole numbers special attention should be given to accuracy and speed. In setting up numbers for multiplication we place units under units, tens under tens, hundreds under hundreds, etc., just as we did in addition and subtraction.

For example:

$$\begin{array}{r} 2643 \\ 679 \\ \hline 23787 \\ 18501 \\ 15858 \\ \hline 1{,}794{,}597 \end{array}$$

In this example, the 679 is called the *multiplier*, the 2643 is known as the *multiplicand*, and the 1,794,597 is referred to as the *product*. Thus the number which is to be multiplied is called the multiplicand. The number which shows how many times the multiplicand is to be taken is called the multiplier. The result obtained by multiplying two numbers is called the product.

Casting out nines can be applied as an interesting and practical check for multiplication of whole numbers. Here we shall need the rule, *the excess of the product is equal to the product of the excesses.*

Thus multiply:

$$\begin{array}{rcr} 382 & \rightarrow & 4 \\ \times\ 68 & \rightarrow & \times\ 5 \\ \hline 3056 & & 20 \\ 2292 & & \\ \hline 25{,}976 & \rightarrow\ 11 \rightarrow & 2 \end{array}$$

Notice that in the product, 25,976, we might just as well drop 2 and 7 as well as 9; adding 5 and 6 we get 11, which reduces to 2.

EXERCISE 4

Multiply:

1. 239 × 67	2. 896 × 78	3. 6,783 × 238
4. 8,579 × 493	5. 9,785 × 8,999	6. 8,934 × 7,647
7. 23,682 × 4,579	8. 67,588 × 6,987	9. 89,787 × 99,875
10. 79,639 × 608	11. 687,459 × 7,005	12. 837,987 × 7,000
13. 9,602,509 × 5,040	14. 7,803,680 × 4,009	15. 39,804,307 × 9,007
16. 24,785,600 × 69,007		

17. Write in words the numbers to be multiplied together in problem 15.

18. Write in words the numbers to be multiplied together in problem 16.

Multiply:

19. 999,687,459
       70,809

20. 897,698,547
       500,903

21. Find the cost of each group of items:
(*a*) Fifteen dish towels at 30 cents each.
(*b*) Four dozen dish cloths at two for 25 cents.
(*c*) Thirty-five feet of chain at 29 cents per foot.

22. What are the gross earnings of a clerk who works 40 hours at $1.80 per hour, 8 hours at $2.70 per hour, and 6 hours at $3.60 per hour?

23. Find the cost of 82 four-cent stamps, 24 seven-cent, and 35 six-cent stamps.

24. How many square feet of window area are there in a wall which has 4 windows each measuring 3 feet by 7 feet?

25. How many cubic feet of air does a room 18 feet by 26 feet by 9 feet contain?

26. What is the cost of equipping a corps of 80 men with uniforms at $88.50 each?

27. How many pounds of food are needed to feed 420 men for 15 days, if each man eats 8 pounds of food per day?

28. What is the cost of 8 aircraft if each costs $2,325,500.00?

29. How far does a car travel in 5 minutes if it goes at a rate of 88 feet per second? (Hint: Distance equals rate times time.)

30. What is the cost of 25 three-cent stamps, 12 five-cent stamps and 20 six-cent stamps?

6. DIVIDING WHOLE NUMBERS

In dividing whole numbers, the number which we are dividing, called the *dividend,* and the number we are dividing by, called the *divisor,* are placed in a special form. The answer is called the *quotient,* and the remainder, if there is one other than zero, is written over the divisor beside the quotient. *Division* is the inverse of multiplication. By this statement we mean that if we multiply by a number and then divide the result by the same number, the final result is the original number. Thus:

$$18 \times 5 = 90 \text{ and } 90 \div 5 = 18$$

Consider the example and divide 6784 by 97.

$$
\begin{array}{rr@{\,}l}
 & 69 & \text{quotient} \\
\text{divisor } 97 \,/ & \overline{6784} & \text{dividend} \\
 & 582 & \\
\cline{2-2}
 & 964 & \\
 & 873 & \\
\cline{2-2}
 & 91 & \text{remainder}
\end{array}
$$

The complete result of the division is $69\frac{91}{97}$. To check this result multiply the quotient by the divisor and add the remainder.

Thus:

$$
\begin{array}{r}
69 \\
\times\, 97 \\
\hline
483 \\
621 \\
\hline
6693
\end{array}
\qquad\qquad
\begin{array}{r}
6693 \\
+\, 91 \\
\hline
6784
\end{array}
$$

Division may be considered in at least two different ways.

First: Division is the process of measuring to find how many times one number is contained in another. The procedure may be carried out by repeated subtraction or by actual measurement. Thus, 8 inches would be contained in 53 inches 6 times, with a remainder of 5 inches. We find therefore that $8\,/\overline{53} = 6\frac{5}{8}$.

Second: Division is a process of partitioning or separating a quantity into a number of equal parts. Thus, to divide 5 into 35 is the same as to find one-fifth of 35. To divide a quantity by 5 is to find one-fifth of it. If 5 boys share 35 cents, each one receives one-fifth of 35 cents, or 7 cents.

Another check for division is by casting out nines. For example check $38\,/\overline{4631}$ by casting out nines.

$$
\begin{array}{rl}
 & 121 \;\; \text{r } 33 \\
38\,/ & \overline{4631} \\
 & 38 \\
\cline{2-2}
 & \;\;83 \\
 & \;\;76 \\
\cline{2-2}
 & \;\;\;\;71 \\
 & \;\;\;\;38 \\
\cline{2-2}
 & \;\;\;\;33
\end{array}
$$

Standard check: $38 \times 121 + 33 = 4631$

$$\begin{array}{lcccl} \text{Casting out nines:} & 2 \times 4 & + & 6 & = 5 \\ \text{Excess of:} & 8 & + & 6 & = 5 \end{array}$$

EXERCISE 5

Divide and check.

1. $83\,/\overline{\,4{,}767}$
2. $67\,/\overline{\,8{,}342}$
3. $267\,/\overline{\,5{,}783}$
4. $393\,/\overline{\,6{,}747}$
5. $7007\,/\overline{\,63{,}409}$
6. $6{,}137\,/\overline{\,74{,}577}$
7. $8648\,/\overline{\,772{,}114}$
8. $4{,}563\,/\overline{\,453{,}225}$
9. $27{,}457\,/\overline{\,437{,}629}$
10. $36{,}589\,/\overline{\,237{,}669}$
11. $223{,}662\,/\overline{\,824{,}679}$
12. $436{,}892\,/\overline{\,647{,}932}$
13. $567{,}883\,/\overline{\,1{,}723{,}459}$
14. $639{,}887\,/\overline{\,822{,}001}$
15. $7{,}642{,}999\,/\overline{\,9{,}342{,}666}$
16. $6{,}457{,}337\,/\overline{\,45{,}347{,}998}$
17. $18{,}000{,}007\,/\overline{\,59{,}377{,}992}$
18. $16{,}247{,}335\,/\overline{\,43{,}662{,}887}$
19. $683\,/\overline{\,252{,}693{,}447}$
20. $799\,/\overline{\,357{,}998{,}479}$

21. How many strips of wood 14 inches long can be cut from a board 196 inches long?

22. How many inches long would each of 6 equal parts of a board 192 inches long have to be?

23. How many miles per gallon does a car travel if it travels 612 miles on 36 gallons of gasoline?

24. How many cars 16 feet long could you place end to end along 3 miles of pavement? (5280 feet = 1 mile.)

25. How many dollars does each one of 225 workers receive as a bonus, if each receives an equal share out of $78,750?

26. A corporation declares an extra dividend of $6,352,422.40 on its 496,283 shares of stock. What is the extra dividend per share?

27. How many 50-pound sacks of poultry feed at $2.30 per sack can be purchased for $103.50?

28. How many gallons of paint at $6.59 per gallon can be bought for $164.75?

29. How many cars 16 feet long can be placed end to end along 5 miles of pavement?

30. How many 50-pound sacks of poultry feed at $2.40 per sack can be purchased for $780.00?

31–45. Check problems 1–15 of this Exercise by casting out nines.

7. THE ROMAN NOTATION FOR NUMBERS

There was a time in Europe when the Roman system of notation was the most popular method of writing numbers. The system is still used rather frequently today for recording dates, numbering chapters in books, and for artistic purposes. The symbols we use today for writing numbers in the Roman notation are given in Table 1.

TABLE 1

Roman Numerals

Our Number	Roman Symbol
1	I
5	V
10	X
50	L
100	C
500	D
1000	M

Three principles are used to form numbers with Roman numerals: (1) addition, (2) multiplication, (3) subtraction.

The principle of addition is illustrated as follows:

$$\text{XXVIII} = \text{X} + \text{X} + \text{V} + \text{I} + \text{I} + \text{I} = 28$$

The principle of multiplication means that drawing a bar over a number multiplies that number by 1000.

For example: $\overline{\text{XXVIII}} = 28{,}000$; $\overline{\text{CCC}} = 300{,}000$

The principle of subtraction is used in writing all fours and nines. It is not used in any other numbers.

For instance:

$$4 = \text{IV}, 9 = \text{IX}, 40 = \text{XL}, 90 = \text{XC}, 400 = \text{CD}, 900 = \text{CM}$$

In writing numbers with Roman numerals, it is recommended that the following rule be followed: First write the thousands, then the hundreds, then the tens, and last of all, the units.

Following this rule we write 87 as LXXXVII and not as XIIIC. Also 632 would be written as DCXXXII and not as CCCCMXXXII.

Other illustrations of numbers correctly written by the Roman system are:

$$3264 = \text{MMMCCLXIV or } \overline{\text{III}}\text{CCLXIV}$$
$$29{,}897 = \overline{\text{XXIX}}\text{DCCCXCVII}$$
$$648{,}753 = \overline{\text{DCXLVIII}}\text{DCCLIII}$$

EXERCISE 6

Write the following in the Roman notation.

1. 6 2. 14 3. 23
4. 37 5. 46 6. 59
7. 64 8. 78 9. 82
10. 95 11. 103 12. 247
13. 649 14. 2352 15. 8683
16. 20,893 17. 425,753 18. 632,923

Write the following according to our method of notation.

19. XX 20. XIII
21. XXXVII 22. XLVI
23. LVIII 24. LXVI
25. LXXIII 26. LXXXVIII
27. XCII 28. CIV
29. CCXXVIII 30. CDXXXVI
31. DCCCXLIII 32. CMLXXXII
33. $\overline{\text{VI}}$CDXLVII 34. $\overline{\text{XXII}}$DXC
35. $\overline{\text{CCCLII}}$DCXXXVII 36. DCCXXXVII

EXERCISE 7
REVIEW

Write the following numbers in words.

1. 8354
2. 12,567
3. 42,684,342
4. 748,573,678
5. 36,743,483,724

6. A state collects $123,729,543 in taxes in a certain year. Write the amount of taxes in words.

7. A company has a gross income of $547,619,783 in a certain year. Write this income in words.

8. A fraternity has 25 gallons of wine in a barrel. If 3 gallons are taken out each day and 2 gallons put in at night, in how many days will the barrel be empty?

9. A farmer counted his eggs by twos, threes, fours, fives, and sixes and had one left each time. He then counted them by sevens and none was left. What is the least number he could have had?

10. Write in numbers: five billion, four hundred thirty-two million, eight hundred sixteen thousand, three hundred twenty-five.

11. Write in numbers: sixteen trillion, seven hundred forty-six billion, eight hundred twelve million, seven hundred sixty-nine thousand, five hundred four.

12. Add:
```
7832
 609
3543
  20
 929
----
```

13. Add:
```
2573
 164
7009
6538
 807
----
```

14. Check the addition in problem 12 by casting out nines.

15. Check the addition in problem 13 by casting out nines.

16. Multiply:
```
60,509
 8,008
------
```

17. Multiply:
```
748,919
  7,069
-------
```

18. Check the multiplication in problem 16 by casting out nines.

19. Check the multiplication in problem 17 by casting out nines.

20. Table 2 is the monthly expense report for the sales depart-

TABLE 2

	Automobile					
Salesman	Gas and Oil	Other	Hotel	Meals	Entertainment of Customers	Totals
Bones	$ 75	$25	$ 92	$148	$72	
Brown	82	28	98	162	85	
Jacks	102	36	110	176	96	
James	96	32	104	172	93	
Rash	120	45	123	169	88	
Stillwater	112	38	112	156	79	
Totals						

ment of the Wear Longer Shoe Manufacturing Company for the month of July, 1958. Complete the report by finding the totals as indicated.

21. The sales made by the salesmen for the Eat-mor Ice Cream Company for the week of May 12 through 17 are given in Table 3. Complete the report.

TABLE 3

Salesman	Monday	Tuesday	Wednesday	Thursday	Friday	Saturday	Totals
Brock	$168	$213	$321	$362	$384	$424	
Casper	234	116	462	325	139	146	
Moore	348	216	285	462	318	269	
Venuti	418	426	439	442	456	213	
Welch	214	153	342	266	316	248	
Totals							

22. A flour mill averages 3842 barrels a day. (1 barrel = 196 pounds of flour.) On the average, how many 25-pound sacks can be filled from one day's output?

23. John works in a machine shop and has made the following castings: 380 pounds, 260 pounds, 325 pounds, 42 pounds, and 128 pounds. What will the castings be worth at 14 cents per pound?

Write the following numbers in words.

24. 43,749,692,073

25. 964,382,463,839

26. Mary has saved $42.29 and wants to buy a coat marked down to $57.88. How much does she need?

27. The goal in a fund raising campaign is $83,450. If $72,406.25 has been raised, how much more is needed to reach the goal?

28. Find the gross earnings of a man who works 40 hours at $2.10 per hour, 6 hours at $3.22 per hour, and 4 hours at $4.20 per hour.

29. How many inches long would each of 12 equal parts of a board 276 inches long have to be?

30. How many dollars does each one of 732 workers receive as a bonus, if each receives an equal share out of $237,900?

CHAPTER THREE

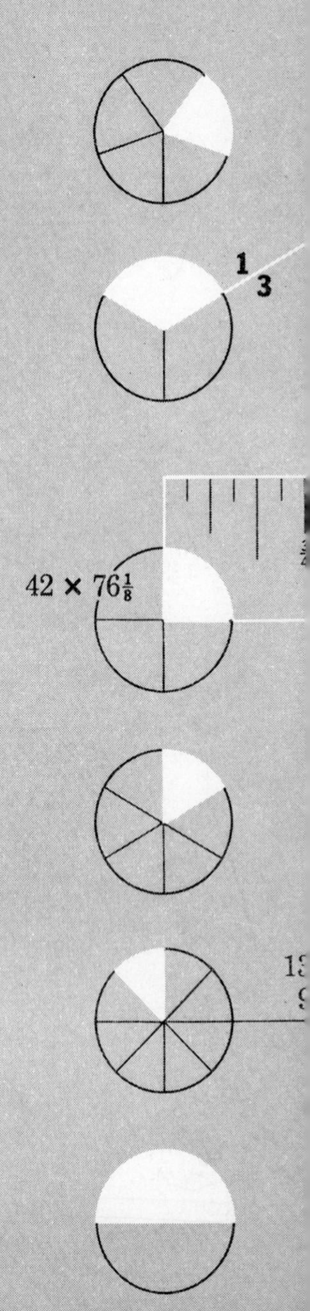

FRACTIONS

1. ADDING AND SUBTRACTING PROPER FRACTIONS

A fraction represents one or more of the equal parts of a unit. Thus, $\frac{5}{8}$ inch represents the length obtained if 1 inch is divided into 8 equal parts and 5 of those parts are taken (Figure 1).

In the number $\frac{5}{8}$, the 8 gives the fraction the name eighths, and is called the *denominator;* the 5 states the number of equal parts which are taken, and is called the *numerator*. The numerator and denominator referred to together are called the *terms* of the fraction. Fractions which have no restrictions upon the size of the terms are called common fractions. A simple fraction has integral terms, that is, terms that are whole numbers. A simple fraction is called proper if the numerator is less than the denominator, otherwise it is called improper. Thus $\frac{3}{8}$ is a proper fraction whereas $\frac{5}{4}$ is an improper fraction. Similarly, $\frac{6}{6}$ is an improper fraction, while $\frac{5}{6}$ is a proper fraction.

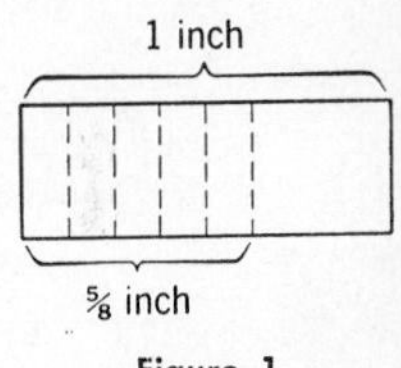

Figure 1

Equivalent fractions are fractions which *represent the same portion or part of a whole quantity*. Thus, $\frac{5}{8}$ of 1 inch is equivalent to $\frac{10}{16}$ of 1 inch. Five-eighths of 1 inch is equivalent to $\frac{20}{32}$ of 1 inch. Five-eighths of 1 inch is equivalent to $\frac{25}{40}$ of 1 inch. Also $\frac{200}{400}$ of 1 dollar is equivalent to $\frac{1}{2}$ of 1 dollar, and $\frac{50}{100}$ of 1 dollar is equivalent to $\frac{1}{2}$ of 1 dollar.

Equivalent fractions can always be changed to identical fractions either by multiplying both terms of one fraction by the same number or by dividing both terms of one fraction by a suitable number. For example:

$$\frac{18}{27} = \frac{18 \div 9}{27 \div 9} = \frac{2}{3}; \quad \text{and} \quad \frac{35}{63} = \frac{35 \div 7}{63 \div 7} = \frac{5}{9}$$

Here we have reduced the fractions $^{18}/_{27}$ and $^{35}/_{63}$. Also consider:

$$\frac{2}{5} = \frac{2 \times 20}{5 \times 20} = \frac{40}{100} \quad \text{and} \quad \frac{3}{8} = \frac{3 \times 45}{8 \times 45} = \frac{135}{360}$$

Here we have changed the fractions $^2/_5$ and $^3/_8$ into equivalent fractions containing larger numbers. In this paragraph we have seen in operation the *Fundamental Principle of Fractions,* which states that multiplying or dividing both terms of a fraction by the same number does not change its value.

We say that $^{18}/_{27}$ has been *reduced to lower terms* and that $^2/_5$ has been *changed to higher terms.* A simple fraction may be changed to higher terms by multiplying its terms by an integer greater than one. In this way, numerous equivalent fractions may be obtained. Thus:

$$\frac{2}{3} = \frac{2 \times 8}{3 \times 8} = \frac{16}{24}, \quad \text{or} \quad \frac{2}{3} = \frac{2 \times 30}{3 \times 30} = \frac{60}{90}$$

Two simple fractions can generally be changed to fractions equivalent to the given ones, and having a *common denominator.* For example, $^2/_3$ and $^3/_4$ are equivalent to $^8/_{12}$ and $^9/_{12}$. The fractions $^8/_{12}$ and $^9/_{12}$ may now be added to give $^{17}/_{12}$, since the 8 and the 9 both count the same thing, namely, twelfths.

Again, $^5/_8$ and $^7/_{12}$ are equivalent to $\frac{5 \times 3}{8 \times 3}$ and $\frac{7 \times 2}{12 \times 2}$, or $^5/_8$ and $^7/_{12}$ are equivalent to $^{15}/_{24}$ and $^{14}/_{24}$, respectively. The difference between $^5/_8$ and $^7/_{12}$ is thus found to be $^1/_{24}$, since we can subtract $^{14}/_{24}$ from $^{15}/_{24}$.

EXERCISE 1

Change the following fractions to equivalent fractions with higher terms or lower terms, as required. (Fill in the spaces.)

1. $\frac{3}{4} = \frac{}{8}, \frac{3}{4} = \frac{}{12}, \frac{3}{4} = \frac{}{100}, \frac{3}{4} = \frac{24}{}.$

2. Change $\frac{2}{3}$ and $\frac{3}{4}$ both to 12ths.

3. Change $\frac{3}{8}$ and $\frac{5}{12}$ both to 24ths.

4. Change $\frac{2}{3}$, $\frac{10}{18}$, $\frac{12}{27}$, $\frac{6}{54}$, $\frac{7}{3}$, $\frac{1}{1}$, $\frac{3}{1}$, all to 9ths.

5. Change $\frac{1}{4}$, $\frac{2}{3}$, $\frac{5}{12}$, $\frac{1}{2}$, $\frac{3}{8}$, $\frac{9}{4}$, $\frac{14}{48}$, $\frac{2}{1}$, to 24ths.

6. Change $\frac{1}{4}$, $\frac{5}{16}$, $\frac{3}{8}$, $\frac{11}{8}$, $\frac{1}{2}$, $\frac{3}{4}$, $\frac{10}{64}$, $\frac{3}{1}$, to 32nds.

7. How many quarts are there in 1 and $\frac{3}{4}$ gallons?

8. How many pints are there in 3 quarts? How many pints are there in 3 gallons?

9. How many ounces are there in $1\frac{3}{4}$ pounds? (16 ounces equal 1 pound.)

10. Which is larger, two-thirds of 1 foot or three-fourths of 1 foot? How much is the difference?

11. Change $\frac{2}{5}$ and $\frac{3}{8}$ both to 40ths.

12. Change $\frac{5}{16}$ and $\frac{4}{9}$ both to 144ths.

13. Change $\frac{2}{3}$, $\frac{5}{8}$, $\frac{15}{48}$, $\frac{3}{16}$, 1, 4, all to 48ths.

14. How many quarts are there in $3\frac{1}{4}$ gallons?

15. How many pints are there in 8 quarts? How many pints are there in 10 gallons?

16. How many ounces are there in $4\frac{1}{4}$ pounds?

17. Which is larger, three-fifths of 1 mile or four-sevenths of 1 mile? How much is the difference?

18. Change the following fractions to equivalent fractions with higher terms or lower terms, as required. (Fill in the spaces.)

$$\frac{5}{6} = \frac{\quad}{30}, \quad \frac{5}{6} = \frac{40}{\quad}, \quad \frac{3}{10} = \frac{\quad}{100}, \quad \frac{9}{25} = \frac{108}{\quad}$$

If two fractions have the same denominator we may add them by adding the numerators. For instance: $\frac{1}{5} + \frac{2}{5} = \frac{3}{5}$

If the fractions do not have the same denominator we must make an adjustment that will give them the same denominator. In the case of $\frac{1}{2} + \frac{3}{4}$, for example, we change the $\frac{1}{2}$ to $\frac{2}{4}$ by multiplying both numerator and denominator by 2. That is, $\frac{1}{2} \times \frac{2}{2} = \frac{2}{4}$. Then $\frac{1}{2} + \frac{3}{4}$ becomes $\frac{2}{4} + \frac{3}{4} = \frac{5}{4}$.

Another approach to be used in adding fractions follows: Consider now $\frac{2}{3} + \frac{5}{18} + \frac{9}{25}$. Find the *Lowest Common Denominator* (L.C.D.) of the three denominators. The lowest common denominator is the smallest quantity divisible by all the denominators under consideration. In order to proceed further, let us break each denominator into its prime factors. A *factor* of a number is any exact divisor of the number. Thus, the factors of 18 are 1, 2, 3, 6, 9, and 18. *Prime factors* are factors which may be divided only by themselves and 1. In the factors of 18, for example, 1, 2, and 3 are primes, since they may be divided only by themselves and 1. Six is not a prime. since it may be divided by itself, 1, 2, and 3. Nine is not a prime, since it may be divided by itself, 1, and 3.

Consider $3/8 + 5/12$. Let us write 8 in terms of its prime factors, $2 \cdot 2 \cdot 2$. We also shall write 12 in terms of its prime factors $2 \cdot 2 \cdot 3$. Thus: $\frac{3}{8} + \frac{5}{12} = \frac{3}{2 \cdot 2 \cdot 2} + \frac{5}{2 \cdot 2 \cdot 3}$

In finding the lowest common denominator of the denominators 8 and 12, we must find a denominator that provides for all prime factors the greatest number of times each prime factor appears in each denominator. Now let us write the lowest common denominator of the denominators $2 \cdot 2 \cdot 2$ and $2 \cdot 2 \cdot 3$. This lowest common denominator is $2 \cdot 2 \cdot 2 \cdot 3$, rather than $2 \cdot 2 \cdot 2 \cdot 2 \cdot 2 \cdot 3$. We do not list the 2 twos under the 5 because they are already provided for in the 3 twos which appear as prime factors of the denominator $2 \cdot 2 \cdot 2$. We list the 3 which appears under the 5; otherwise we would not make provision for it in the lowest common denominator.

Now:

$$\frac{3}{8} + \frac{5}{12} = \frac{3}{2 \cdot 2 \cdot 2} + \frac{5}{2 \cdot 2 \cdot 3} = \frac{3 \cdot 3}{2 \cdot 2 \cdot 2 \cdot 3} + \frac{5 \cdot 2}{2 \cdot 2 \cdot 2 \cdot 3}$$

$$= \frac{3 \cdot 3 + 5 \cdot 2}{2 \cdot 2 \cdot 2 \cdot 3} = \frac{9 + 10}{24} = \frac{19}{24}$$

Looking again at the example $2/3 + 5/18 + 9/25$, we express each denominator in terms of prime factors. Then:

$$\frac{2}{1 \cdot 3} + \frac{5}{2 \cdot 3 \cdot 3} + \frac{9}{5 \cdot 5} = ?$$

In finding the lowest common denominator of a series of denominators, we must write a denominator that provides for all factors the greatest number of times each factor appears in each denominator. Now let us write the lowest common denominator of the denominators 1·3, 2·3·3, and 5·5. We will not write two threes to the right of the two because there is already one three in the set of numbers in the lowest common denominator.

Then: $$\frac{2}{1\cdot 3} + \frac{5}{2\cdot 3\cdot 3} + \frac{9}{5\cdot 5} =$$

$$\frac{?}{1\cdot 3\cdot 2\cdot 3\cdot 5\cdot 5} =$$

$$\frac{2(2\cdot 3\cdot 5\cdot 5) + 5(5\cdot 5) + 9(1\cdot 3\cdot 2\cdot 3)}{1\cdot 3\cdot 2\cdot 3\cdot 5\cdot 5} =$$

$$\frac{300 + 125 + 162}{350} = \frac{587}{350}$$

Let us go through the steps in the foregoing simplification. We find that the first denominator, 1·3, if it were to be made like the lowest common denominator, would need to be multiplied by 2·3·5·5. Therefore, we multiply the numerator by 2·3·5·5 in order to treat the numerator in the same way we treated the denominator. We see that the second denominator, 2·3·3, if it were to be made like the lowest common denominator, would need to be multiplied by 5·5. Therefore, we multiply the numerator by 5·5. We observe that the third denominator, 5·5, if it were to be made like the L.C.D., would need to be multiplied by 3·2·3. Since all denominators are alike, we may add the numerators and simplify as indicated in the foregoing illustration.

The fraction $5/4$ we have already referred to as an improper fraction. The expression $1\frac{1}{4}$ is a mixed number. A mixed number is the sum of an integer and a simple fraction. By integer we mean any of the numbers 1, 2, 3, etc. Notice that $1\frac{1}{4}$ means $1 + 1/4$.

In subtracting fractions the operation with the denominators is identical with that of adding fractions. However, the numerators are subtracted rather than added.

Consider $5/6 - 2/3 = ?$ The lowest common denominator of 6 and 3 is 6. Now the denominator 6 goes into the lowest common denominator 6, one time and 1 times 5 equals 5. The denominator 3 goes into the lowest common denominator 6, two times and 2 times 2 equals 4. Now:

$$\frac{5}{6} - \frac{2}{3} = \frac{5}{6} - \frac{4}{6} = \frac{5-4}{6} = \frac{1}{6}$$

Another example is $\frac{2}{3} + \frac{3}{8} - \frac{3}{5} = ?$ The lowest common denominator for the 3, 8, and 5 is 120. Then:

$$\frac{2}{3} + \frac{3}{8} - \frac{3}{5} = \frac{80}{120} + \frac{45}{120} - \frac{72}{120} = \frac{80 + 45 - 72}{120}$$

$$= \frac{125 - 72}{120} = \frac{53}{120}$$

EXERCISE 2

Add and subtract as indicated.

1. $\frac{1}{2} + \frac{1}{2} =$
2. $\frac{1}{3} + \frac{1}{3} =$
3. $\frac{2}{5} + \frac{3}{5} =$
4. $\frac{1}{4} + \frac{3}{4} =$
5. $\frac{5}{6} - \frac{1}{6} =$
6. $\frac{3}{7} - \frac{2}{7} =$
7. $\frac{3}{5} + \frac{4}{5} =$
8. $\frac{4}{5} - \frac{3}{5} =$
9. $\frac{2}{3} + \frac{3}{4} =$
10. $\frac{2}{7} + \frac{3}{8} =$
11. $\frac{5}{9} - \frac{1}{5} =$
12. $\frac{3}{4} - \frac{2}{5} =$
13. $\frac{3}{7} + \frac{2}{3} + \frac{4}{7} =$
14. $\frac{1}{8} + \frac{3}{5} + \frac{3}{8} =$
15. $\frac{4}{15} + \frac{2}{3} + \frac{4}{5} =$
16. $\frac{5}{8} + \frac{3}{4} - \frac{2}{3} =$
17. $\frac{3}{16} + \frac{2}{5} - \frac{3}{4} =$
18. $\frac{6}{7} + \frac{3}{8} - \frac{1}{4} =$
19. $\frac{6}{7} + \frac{4}{5} + \frac{8}{9} + \frac{2}{3} =$
20. $\frac{2}{9} + \frac{5}{16} + \frac{5}{8} + \frac{7}{9} =$
21. $\frac{4}{16} + \frac{3}{8} + \frac{8}{9} - \frac{2}{15} - \frac{3}{7} =$
22. $\frac{2}{5} - \frac{3}{7} + \frac{15}{45} - \frac{2}{11} =$
23. $\frac{6}{19} - \frac{5}{24} =$
24. $\frac{8}{17} - \frac{12}{35} =$
25. $\frac{5}{154} + \frac{16}{247} =$
26. $\frac{6}{123} + \frac{4}{235} =$
27. $\frac{4}{15} + \frac{2}{3} + \frac{3}{7} + \frac{8}{9} - \frac{3}{16} =$
28. $\frac{3}{4} + \frac{5}{9} - \frac{6}{17} - \frac{3}{19} =$
29. $\frac{3}{16} + \frac{1}{32} + \frac{7}{10} - \frac{3}{7} =$
30. $\frac{1}{5} + \frac{2}{3} + \frac{3}{15} + \frac{5}{6} + \frac{8}{9} =$

31. The heirs to the Johnson Estate receive shares of $\frac{1}{4}$, $\frac{1}{8}$, $\frac{2}{9}$, and $\frac{1}{3}$. The rest is left to charities. What fraction of the estate is left to charities? (Add the shares, and subtract their sum from 1.)

32. In sharing a Christmas bonus, four employees receive shares as follows: $\frac{1}{10}$, $\frac{2}{5}$, $\frac{1}{8}$, and $\frac{3}{20}$ respectively. What fraction will represent the share of the fifth employee? Assume that the five share the whole bonus.

33. In attempting to subscribe for a block of stock in a company, 6 men put in amounts represented by the following fractions: $\frac{1}{30}$, $\frac{1}{5}$, $\frac{1}{20}$, $\frac{1}{40}$, $\frac{3}{8}$, and $\frac{2}{15}$. Two of the men then sell

$\frac{1}{18}$ and $\frac{2}{15}$ of the block. How much of the block is left to be subscribed?

34. How much larger is $\frac{3}{4}$ than $\frac{5}{8}$?

35. How much larger is $\frac{9}{16}$ than $\frac{3}{8}$?

36. One budget suggests that $\frac{1}{5}$ of income be spent for taxes, $\frac{1}{4}$ for rent, and $\frac{1}{20}$ for insurance. What part of the income is left for other uses?

37. Another budget suggests $\frac{3}{20}$ of income for rent, $\frac{1}{4}$ for groceries, $\frac{1}{8}$ for meat, and $\frac{7}{50}$ for clothing. How much remains for other purposes?

38. Arrange the following fractions in order from largest to smallest: $\frac{5}{18}$, $\frac{3}{25}$, $\frac{4}{7}$, and $\frac{9}{16}$.

39. A carpenter has drill bits with diameters of $\frac{7}{12}$, $\frac{11}{18}$, $\frac{1}{2}$, and $\frac{5}{9}$ inches. Arrange these fractions in order from largest to smallest.

40. Find the total of $\frac{3}{8} + \frac{4}{9} - \frac{5}{36} + \frac{7}{18}$, and subtract it from the total of $\frac{5}{6} + \frac{7}{12} + \frac{17}{18} - \frac{7}{16}$.

2. MULTIPLYING PROPER FRACTIONS

In multiplying two proper fractions we multiply the two numerators to obtain a new numerator and multiply the two denominators to obtain a new denominator. The resulting fraction should be reduced to lowest terms. Thus:

$$\frac{3}{8} \times \frac{2}{15} = \frac{6}{120} = \frac{1}{20}$$

It is frequently preferred to simplify by division as follows:

$$\frac{\overset{1}{\cancel{3}}}{\underset{4}{\cancel{8}}} \times \frac{\overset{1}{\cancel{2}}}{\underset{5}{\cancel{15}}} = \frac{1}{20}$$

Here we have divided the 3 into itself and into the 15. The 3 goes into itself one time and into the 15 five times. The two goes into itself one time and into the 8 four times. Multiplying the two new numerators, we have $1 \times 1 = 1$. Multiplying the two new denominators, we have $4 \times 5 = 20$. The final result is $\frac{1}{20}$.

As another example consider $\frac{2}{3} \times \frac{4}{5} \times \frac{25}{48} \times \frac{9}{14}$.

Let us factor each numerator and denominator into prime factors. Now we have

$$\frac{2}{3} \times \frac{2 \cdot 2}{1 \cdot 5} \times \frac{5 \cdot 5}{2 \cdot 2 \cdot 2 \cdot 2 \cdot 3} \times \frac{3 \cdot 3}{2 \cdot 7} =$$

$$\frac{\overset{1}{\cancel{2}} \times \overset{1}{\cancel{2}} \times \overset{1}{\cancel{2}} \times \overset{1}{\cancel{5}} \times 5 \times \overset{1}{\cancel{3}} \times \overset{1}{\cancel{3}}}{\underset{1}{\cancel{3}} \times \underset{1}{\cancel{5}} \times \underset{1}{\cancel{2}} \times \underset{1}{\cancel{2}} \times \underset{1}{\cancel{2}} \times 2 \times \underset{1}{\cancel{3}} \times 2 \times 7} = \frac{5}{28}$$

Here, the numerator, $2 \times 2 \times 2 \times 5 \times 5 \times 3 \times 3$, consists of all the factors of the numerators, and the denominator, $3 \times 5 \times 2 \times 2 \times 2 \times 2 \times 3 \times 2 \times 7$, consists of all the factors of the denominators. Reduction to lowest terms is simply the dividing out of all factors common to both numerator and denominator and multiplying the remaining numerator terms for a new numerator and the remaining denominator terms for a new denominator. Thus we obtain $5/28$.

EXERCISE 3

Multiply and reduce the answer to lowest terms.

1. $3/5 \times 5/6 =$
2. $4/9 \times 27/64 =$
3. $6/25 \times 5/8 =$
4. $7/30 \times 4/49 =$
5. $15/64 \times 8/45 =$
6. $18/128 \times 64/69 =$
7. $8/17 \times 51/56 =$
8. $23/45 \times 5/46 =$
9. $2/3 \times 9/10 \times 4/27 =$
10. $6/25 \times 5/8 \times 3/4 =$
11. $9/50 \times 25/36 \times 64/91 =$
12. $3/40 \times 20/99 \times 40/53 =$
13. $4/15 \times 25/48 \times 16/55 \times 11/14 =$
14. $12/25 \times 15/84 \times 56/63 \times 69/144 =$
15. $47/66 \times 16/45 \times 92/141 \times 90/164 =$
16. $14/15 \times 19/24 \times 45/57 \times 3/56 =$
17. $65/256 \times 20/47 \times 64/195 \times 188/260 =$
18. $27/52 \times 830/2433 \times 29/83 \times 99/594 =$
19. $6/15 \times 25/48 \times 56/135 \times 91/100 \times 20/49 =$
20. $14/27 \times 81/70 \times 625/900 \times 256/1000 =$
21. What is the cost of $2\frac{3}{4}$ yards of cloth at $1.68 per yard?

22. What is the value of 35 shares of stock at $102\frac{1}{2}$ per share?

23. What is the area of a room $12\frac{3}{4}$ feet long by $16\frac{2}{3}$ feet wide?

Solution: $(12\frac{3}{4}) \times (16\frac{2}{3}) = 12 \times 16 + \frac{2}{3} \times 12 + \frac{3}{4} \times 16 + \frac{2}{3} \times \frac{3}{4} = 192 + 8 + 12 + \frac{1}{2} = 212\frac{1}{2}$ square feet

24. What is the perimeter of the room in problem 23?

25. If a cubic foot of space holds $7\frac{1}{2}$ gallons, how many gallons will a tank hold if its volume is 80 cubic feet?

26. How many ounces are there in $23\frac{3}{4}$ pounds of glue?

27. What is the area, and what is the perimeter of a room which is $20\frac{3}{4}$ feet by $16\frac{1}{2}$ feet?

28. Find the total value of the following lots of shares: 38 shares at $27\frac{1}{2}$, 45 shares at $16\frac{2}{3}$, 70 shares at $43\frac{1}{2}$, and 16 shares at $17\frac{5}{8}$.

29. What is the total weight of 24 candy bars each containing $1\frac{3}{8}$ ounces of candy?

30. What is the volume of a box $8\frac{1}{2}$ inches by $2\frac{3}{4}$ inches by $4\frac{2}{3}$ inches? (volume = length × width × depth)

31. A glass is half full of grape juice and another glass twice the size is one-third full. They are then filled with water and the contents mixed. What part of the mixture is grape juice?

32. The winning team in a bowling contest received $125 as a prize. The team members agreed to divide the money according to the number of games each member of the team had bowled. Find each member's share if the team bowled games as follows: Jack, 42; Moe, 38; Herb, 29; Ed, 36; Frisky, 45; and Carl, 34.

33. An auditorium seats 2000 persons. At a recent entertainment one usher guessed it was three-fourths full, another that it was two-thirds full. The ticket office reported 1700 sales. Which usher (first or second) made the better guess?

34. Harry can do a job in 4 hours. Sam can do the same job in 5 hours. How many hours will it take them to do the work, working together?

3. DIVIDING PROPER FRACTIONS

In dividing simple fractions we may think of the process of division as *measurement* or *partition,* or of *changing to an equivalent fraction* with simpler terms. In each case we may change the problem from one of division to one of multiplication.

Consider the following examples:

A. $3/8 \div 2$ can mean: find $1/2$ of $3/8$. Therefore we have

$$3/8 \div 2 = 1/2 \times 3/8 = 3/16$$

Notice that $3/16$ is one of two equal parts of $3/8$. This is the idea of *partition.*

B. $3 \div 1/4$ can mean find how many times $1/4$ is contained in 3. Since there are 4 quarters in one unit, 3 units contain 3×4 quarters, or 12 quarters. This is the idea of *measurement:* $1/4$ inch is contained in 3 inches, 12 times.

C. $3/4 \div 2/3$ is the same as the fraction $\frac{3/4}{2/3}$. Changing to higher terms we have

$$\frac{3/4}{2/3} = \frac{3/4 \times 12}{2/3 \times 12} = 9/8 = 1\,1/8$$

D. Again, $3/4 \div 2/3$ is the same as $\frac{3/4}{2/3}$, and to change terms we write

$$\frac{3/4}{2/3} = \frac{3/4 \times 3/2}{2/3 \times 3/2} = \frac{3/4 \times 3/2}{1} = 3/4 \times 3/2 = 9/8 \quad \text{or} \quad 1\,1/8$$

Notice that we have changed the problem in division, $3/4 \div 2/3$, to an equivalent problem in multiplication, $3/4 \times 3/2$. This procedure is always possible with simple fractions. Thus:

$$\frac{a}{b} \div \frac{c}{d} = \frac{\frac{a}{b}}{\frac{c}{d}} = \frac{\frac{a}{b} \times \frac{d}{c}}{\frac{c}{d} \times \frac{d}{c}} = \frac{\frac{a}{b} \times \frac{d}{c}}{\frac{c}{d} \times \frac{d}{c}} = \frac{\frac{a}{b} \times \frac{d}{c}}{1}$$

Therefore: $\frac{a}{b} \div \frac{c}{d} = \frac{a}{b} \times \frac{d}{c}.$

We speak of this procedure in division as *inverting the divisor.*

In dividing two proper fractions we invert the divisor and then multiply the two fractions.

For example: $\frac{3}{4} \div \frac{3}{8} = \frac{\overset{1}{\cancel{3}}}{\underset{1}{\cancel{4}}} \times \frac{\overset{2}{\cancel{8}}}{\underset{1}{\cancel{3}}} = 2$

Here we have $3/8$ as the divisor. Upon inverting $3/8$, we obtain $8/3$.

The division process might also be expressed as

$$\frac{\frac{5}{6}}{\frac{25}{126}} = \frac{\overset{1}{\cancel{5}}}{\underset{1}{\cancel{6}}} \times \frac{\overset{21}{\cancel{126}}}{\underset{5}{\cancel{25}}} = \frac{21}{5} = 4\frac{1}{5}$$

In a series of divisions of fractions, such as $\frac{3}{4} \div \frac{1}{2} \div \frac{2}{3}$, we have

$$\frac{3}{4} \times \overset{1}{\cancel{2}} \times \frac{3}{\underset{1}{\cancel{2}}} = \frac{9}{4} \quad \text{or} \quad 2\frac{1}{4}$$

EXERCISE 4

Divide and reduce the answer to lowest terms.

1. $\frac{4}{5} \div \frac{12}{25} =$
2. $\frac{6}{11} \div \frac{2}{33} =$
3. $\frac{2}{3} \div \frac{4}{3} =$
4. $\frac{3}{5} \div \frac{6}{25} =$
5. $\frac{5}{6} \div \frac{25}{36} =$
6. $\frac{2}{5} \div \frac{12}{25} =$
7. $\frac{16}{27} \div \frac{4}{3} =$
8. $\frac{15}{22} \div \frac{5}{2} =$
9. $\frac{125}{256} \div \frac{25}{32} =$
10. $\frac{81}{141} \div \frac{27}{94} =$
11. $\dfrac{\frac{8}{9}}{\frac{16}{54}} =$
12. $\dfrac{\frac{14}{17}}{\frac{28}{51}} =$
13. $\dfrac{\frac{25}{39}}{\frac{125}{147}} =$
14. $\dfrac{\frac{150}{260}}{\frac{39}{15}} =$
15. $\frac{4}{5} \div \frac{2}{3} \div \frac{18}{25} =$
16. $\frac{26}{85} \div \frac{13}{15} \div \frac{14}{51} =$
17. $\dfrac{\frac{3}{8} \div \frac{15}{16}}{\frac{4}{7} \div \frac{16}{21}} =$
18. $\dfrac{\frac{6}{17} \div \frac{12}{85}}{\frac{5}{9} \div \frac{25}{27}} =$
19. $\frac{124}{255} \div \frac{42}{55} \div \frac{132}{245} =$
20. $\frac{63}{82} \div \frac{162}{220} \div \frac{88}{108} =$
21. $\frac{5}{18} \div \frac{4}{15} \div \frac{6}{85} \div \frac{25}{48} =$
22. $\frac{3}{40} \div \frac{9}{20} \div \frac{55}{729} \div \frac{81}{192} =$
23. $\frac{8}{25} \div \frac{96}{625} \div \frac{160}{192} \div \frac{22}{54} =$
24. $\frac{17}{42} \div \frac{136}{252} =$
25. $\frac{91}{145} \div \frac{273}{280} =$
26. $\frac{4}{15} \div \frac{120}{225} \div \frac{729}{1025} =$
27. $\dfrac{\frac{6}{19} \div \frac{4}{35}}{\frac{14}{27} \div \frac{38}{81}} =$
28. $\dfrac{\frac{6}{58} \div \frac{4}{36}}{\frac{14}{27} \div \frac{16}{1458}} =$

29. If a car uses $\frac{3}{32}$ gallon of gasoline per mile, how many miles can it travel on 38 gallons of gasoline?

30. How many pieces $\frac{3}{4}$ inch in length can be cut from a bar 24 inches in length if $\frac{1}{8}$ inch is allowed for each cut?

31. A piece of wood $\frac{15}{16}$ inch thick is made by gluing together strips each $\frac{5}{32}$ inch thick. How many strips are there in this piece?

32. If a car uses $\frac{4}{49}$ gallon of gasoline per mile, how many miles does it get to the gallon?

33. How many pieces $\frac{9}{16}$ inch in length can be cut from a bar 54 inches in length if $\frac{1}{8}$ inch is allowed for each cut?

34. A piece of wood $\frac{7}{8}$ inch thick is made by gluing together strips each $\frac{21}{72}$ inch thick. How many strips are there in this piece?

35. A boy can do five-eighths of a job in one day. How long will it take him to do the whole job?

36. A tank can be four-fifths filled in one hour. How long will it take to fill the tank?

37. Jim can mow three-fourths of a lawn in two-thirds of a day. How long will it take him to mow the whole lawn?

38. A student can do one-fourth of an assignment in $\frac{1}{2}$ hour. How long will it take him to do the whole assignment?

4. ADDING AND SUBTRACTING IMPROPER FRACTIONS AND MIXED NUMBERS

As we have already explained, an improper fraction is a fraction whose denominator is smaller than its numerator. Thus $\frac{9}{5}$ is an improper fraction.

In adding and subtracting improper fractions we proceed as we did in the case of proper fractions. For example, $\frac{8}{3} + \frac{14}{3} = ?$ Here the denominators are alike to begin with, and we add the two numerators 8 and 14 to obtain 22. Thus the answer is $\frac{22}{3}$, as an improper fraction, or $7\frac{1}{3}$ as a mixed number.

Now consider $\frac{15}{4} + \frac{13}{5} = ?$ Here the denominators are different. We find the lowest common denominator, which is 20. Now, as indicated before in adding fractions, the denominator 4 goes into the denominator 20, five times. We take five times 15 to obtain 75. The denominator 5 goes into 20, four times. We take four times 13 which is 52. Written in much more convenient form we have

$$\frac{15}{4} + \frac{13}{5} = \frac{75 + 52}{20} = \frac{127}{20} = 6\tfrac{7}{20}$$

As an example of subtracting improper fractions we have $\frac{5}{3} - \frac{6}{5} = ?$ The lowest common denominator of 3 and 5 is 15. The denominator 3 goes into the common denominator 15 five times. Five times the numerator 5 is 25. The denominator 5 goes into the common denominator 15 three times. Three times the numerator 6 is 18. Thus we have in a more convenient form:

$$\frac{25 - 18}{15} = \frac{7}{15}$$

In adding mixed numbers we have three types of approaches. In the first approach we arrange the numbers in a vertical line. In the second we arrange the numbers in a horizontal line. In the third we change the mixed numbers to improper fractions and proceed as in the illustrative examples just given.

In adding $\begin{array}{r} 65\frac{3}{4} \\ 42\frac{7}{8} \\ \hline \end{array}$ we have the numbers arranged in a vertical line. In working this example consider first the proper fractions $\frac{3}{4}$ and $\frac{7}{8}$. Find the common denominator of 4 and 8, which is 8. Dividing the denominator 4 into the common denominator 8 we obtain 2. This number we multiply by the numerator 3, which gives 6. Thus the fraction $\frac{3}{4}$ is changed to an equivalent fraction or $\frac{6}{8}$. Now the problem of adding $\begin{array}{r} 65\frac{3}{4} \\ 42\frac{7}{8} \\ \hline \end{array}$ becomes $\begin{array}{r} 65\ \frac{6}{8} \\ 42\ \frac{7}{8} \\ \hline 107\frac{13}{8} \end{array}$.

Adding the $\frac{6}{8}$ and $\frac{7}{8}$ we have $\frac{13}{8}$. Adding the 65 and 42, we obtain 107. The improper fraction $\frac{13}{8}$ simplifies into $1\frac{5}{8}$. Adding the 1 to 107 we obtain 108, and we write the final answer as $108\frac{5}{8}$.

In combining $65\frac{3}{4} + 42\frac{7}{8}$, we have the numbers arranged in a horizontal line. We may begin by taking the proper fractions $\frac{3}{4}$ and $\frac{7}{8}$ and finding the common denominator 32. Now, as in the preceding example, we convert $\frac{3}{4}$ to its equivalent fraction $\frac{24}{32}$ and change $\frac{7}{8}$ to its equivalent fraction $\frac{28}{32}$. When we add the $\frac{24}{32}$ and the $\frac{28}{32}$, the result is $\frac{52}{32}$ or $1\frac{20}{32}$, which simplifies to $1\frac{5}{8}$. Adding the 65 and the 42 we have 107. Then combining the 1 in the $1\frac{5}{8}$ with the 107, we obtain $65\frac{3}{4} + 42\frac{7}{8} = 108\frac{5}{8}$.

Finally, in adding $65\frac{3}{4}$ and $42\frac{7}{8}$, we may change each of the mixed numbers to improper fractions and combine, as in the section on improper fractions. Let us examine how to change the mixed number $65\frac{3}{4}$ to its equivalent improper fraction. $65\frac{3}{4}$ means 65 plus $\frac{3}{4}$. We must therefore change 65 to fourths in order to add it to $\frac{3}{4}$. Sixty-five equals 260 fourths. Now:

$$\frac{260}{4} + \frac{3}{4} = \frac{263}{4}$$

Thus:

$$65\tfrac{3}{4} + 42\tfrac{7}{8} = \frac{263}{4} + \frac{343}{8} = \frac{526 + 343}{8} = \frac{869}{8} = 108\tfrac{5}{8}$$

In subtracting mixed numbers we may follow any one of the three types of approach previously outlined for the addition of mixed numbers. In the first approach we arrange the numbers in a vertical line. In the second we arrange the numbers in a horizontal line. In the third we change the mixed numbers to improper fractions and then subtract. For example, as an illustration of arranging the numbers in a vertical line, subtract $83\frac{2}{7}$ from $245\frac{5}{6}$.

$$\begin{array}{r} 245\tfrac{5}{6} \\ \underline{83\tfrac{2}{7}} \end{array} \quad \text{becomes} \quad \begin{array}{r} 245\tfrac{35}{42} \\ \underline{83\tfrac{12}{42}} \\ 162\tfrac{23}{42} \end{array}$$

The arrangement of numbers in a horizontal line is illustrated by

$$92\tfrac{3}{4} - 61\tfrac{5}{8} = 92\tfrac{6}{8} - 61\tfrac{5}{8} = 31\tfrac{1}{8}$$

An example of changing mixed numbers to improper fractions and then subtracting is

$$154\tfrac{3}{5} - 27\tfrac{3}{4} = \frac{773}{5} - \frac{111}{4} = \frac{3092 - 555}{20} = \frac{2537}{20} = 126\tfrac{17}{20}$$

EXERCISE 5

Add and subtract as indicated.

1. $2\frac{3}{4} + 5\frac{7}{8} =$

2. $3\frac{4}{7} + 15\frac{3}{5} =$

3. $7\frac{4}{9} + 27\frac{5}{16} =$

4. $81\frac{3}{5} + 26\frac{3}{4} =$

5. $47\frac{3}{8} - 15\frac{5}{7} =$

6. $126\frac{2}{5} - 63\frac{4}{9} =$

7. Add: $\begin{array}{r} 320\frac{15}{16} \\ 126\frac{3}{4} \\ \hline \end{array}$

8. Add: $\begin{array}{r} 224\frac{3}{5} \\ 64\frac{2}{3} \\ \hline \end{array}$

9. Subtract: $\begin{array}{r} 7\frac{3}{8} \\ 5\frac{1}{3} \\ \hline \end{array}$

10. Subtract: $\begin{array}{r} 9\frac{3}{4} \\ 6\frac{2}{5} \\ \hline \end{array}$

11. Subtract: $\begin{array}{r} 93\frac{5}{16} \\ 34\frac{3}{5} \\ \hline \end{array}$

12. Subtract: $\begin{array}{r} 78\frac{9}{17} \\ 34\frac{5}{8} \\ \hline \end{array}$

13. Subtract: $\begin{array}{r} 834\frac{3}{8} \\ 226\frac{5}{9} \\ \hline \end{array}$

14. Subtract: $\begin{array}{r} 625\frac{9}{15} \\ 324\frac{4}{3} \\ \hline \end{array}$

15. $8\frac{3}{7} - 3\frac{5}{8} =$

16. $7\frac{3}{16} - 4\frac{7}{8} =$

17. $19\frac{3}{16} - 14\frac{2}{5} =$

18. $43\frac{3}{7} - 25\frac{4}{9} =$

19. $15\frac{4}{17} + 23\frac{3}{4} - 16\frac{3}{8} =$

20. $82\frac{3}{8} - 20\frac{2}{3} - 40\frac{6}{7} =$

21. $67\frac{9}{17} - 35\frac{3}{4} - 10\frac{1}{2} =$

22. $125\frac{3}{8} + 13\frac{4}{9} - 16\frac{3}{4} =$

23. $\frac{9}{4} + \frac{7}{3} =$

24. $\frac{10}{3} + \frac{11}{4} =$

25. $\frac{18}{7} + \frac{35}{14} + \frac{61}{9} =$

26. $\frac{24}{11} + \frac{16}{13} + \frac{5}{2} =$

27. $\frac{10}{3} + \frac{16}{5} - \frac{42}{17} =$

28. $\frac{28}{9} + \frac{35}{4} - \frac{14}{5} =$

29. $\frac{53}{14} - \frac{5}{3} - \frac{6}{5} =$

Add:

30. $\begin{array}{r} \frac{9}{8} \\ \frac{5}{2} \\ \hline \end{array}$

31. $\begin{array}{r} \frac{37}{5} \\ \frac{8}{3} \\ \frac{9}{4} \\ \hline \end{array}$

32. $\begin{array}{r} \frac{124}{7} \\ \frac{18}{17} \\ \frac{3}{2} \\ \hline \end{array}$

33. $\begin{array}{r} \frac{15}{8} \\ \frac{19}{14} \\ \frac{65}{3} \\ \hline \end{array}$

34. $\begin{array}{r} \frac{125}{4} \\ \frac{435}{56} \\ \frac{325}{14} \\ \hline \end{array}$

Subtract in each of the following problems.

35. $\frac{8}{5}$
$\frac{4}{3}$

36. $\frac{11}{8}$
$\frac{25}{24}$

37. $\frac{100}{49}$
$\frac{200}{147}$

38. $\frac{72}{17}$
$\frac{319}{204}$

Combine as indicated:

39. $83\frac{5}{8} + \frac{125}{4} - 9\frac{3}{7} =$

40. $\frac{95}{14} - 3\frac{2}{5} - \frac{25}{18} =$

41. Bob is building a table top in his shop from 4 pieces of board. One board is $4\frac{3}{8}$ inches wide, the second is $6\frac{2}{5}$ inches wide, and the third is $3\frac{1}{2}$ inches wide. How wide should the fourth board be in order for the top to be $18\frac{3}{4}$ inches wide?

42. A piece of cloth $16\frac{4}{5}$ yards long shrank $1\frac{1}{8}$ yards in bleaching. How long was the cloth after bleaching?

43. The total length of two pieces of molding must be $12\frac{3}{4}$ feet. If one piece is $7\frac{2}{3}$ feet long, what is the proper length for the second piece?

44. A rope 25 feet long is desired. Two pieces, $6\frac{3}{4}$ feet and $10\frac{1}{2}$ feet long are on hand. How long a piece must be brought, assuming that the pieces are not joined to form a closed circle and that each joining requires $\frac{5}{6}$ of a foot.

45. A flock of chickens is fed the following amounts on each of 5 days: $12\frac{1}{2}$ pounds, $10\frac{3}{4}$ pounds, $11\frac{4}{5}$ pounds, $13\frac{2}{3}$ pounds, and $12\frac{5}{6}$ pounds. If 100 pounds of feed were on hand to begin with, and $\frac{3}{4}$ of a pound were wasted during the 5-day period, how much feed was still on hand at the end of the 5 days?

46. Mr. Black has the following hours on his time card for a 10-day period: $6\frac{3}{4}$, $7\frac{4}{5}$, $9\frac{1}{2}$, $8\frac{1}{6}$, $7\frac{5}{12}$, $8\frac{1}{4}$, $9\frac{4}{15}$, $8\frac{7}{12}$, $7\frac{3}{5}$, and $14\frac{5}{6}$ hours. He is to get overtime for all hours in excess of 80. Does he have any overtime coming to him? If so, how many hours?

47. A piece of cloth $25\frac{3}{4}$ yards long shrinks $1\frac{7}{8}$ yards while

being bleached. How long a piece remains after the bleaching process?

48. In the DZ Dog Kennel the following amounts of dog feed are used each month for a year: $45\frac{2}{3}$ pounds, $62\frac{3}{5}$ pounds, $54\frac{3}{4}$ pounds, $76\frac{5}{16}$ pounds, $64\frac{7}{8}$ pounds, $58\frac{1}{4}$ pounds, $63\frac{5}{8}$ pounds, $53\frac{7}{16}$ pounds, $62\frac{3}{4}$ pounds, $75\frac{1}{3}$ pounds, $52\frac{5}{8}$ pounds, and $61\frac{4}{5}$ pounds. How many 25-pound sacks of dog feed should be purchased to provide for the kennel during this 12-month period?

49. Bill works for the following hours after school for 5 days: $2\frac{2}{3}$, $5\frac{4}{5}$, $3\frac{3}{4}$, $2\frac{3}{10}$, and $6\frac{5}{12}$. Find the total number of hours he works.

50. If $63\frac{3}{4}$ feet of fencing are on hand and $125\frac{2}{3}$ feet in frontage are to be fenced, how many feet must be purchased, allowing $\frac{5}{12}$ foot for overlapping of the 2 pieces?

5. MULTIPLYING IMPROPER FRACTIONS AND MIXED NUMBERS

In multiplying improper fractions we may follow one of several different approaches. (1) We may multiply the numerators for a new numerator and multiply the denominators for a new denominator. The resulting fraction should always be reduced to lowest terms. For example: $\frac{9}{4} \times \frac{32}{27} = \frac{288}{108} = \frac{8}{3} = 2\frac{2}{3}$. Here we multiplied 32 and 9 to obtain 288 and multiplied 4 by 27 to obtain 108. (2) We can multiply improper fractions in the following way: Break up each numerator and each denominator into prime factors. Thus:

$$\frac{9}{4} \times \frac{32}{27} = \frac{3\cdot 3}{2\cdot 2} \times \frac{2\cdot 2\cdot 2\cdot 2\cdot 2}{3\cdot 3\cdot 3} = \frac{3\cdot 3\cdot 2\cdot 2\cdot 2\cdot 2\cdot 2}{2\cdot 2\cdot 3\cdot 3\cdot 3}$$

The fraction is reduced to lowest terms by dividing out all factors common to both numerator and denominator and multiplying the remaining numerator terms for a new numerator and the remaining denominator terms for a new denominator. Now:

$$\frac{\overset{1}{\cancel{3}}\cdot \overset{1}{\cancel{3}}\cdot \overset{1}{\cancel{2}}\cdot \overset{1}{\cancel{2}}\cdot 2\cdot 2\cdot 2}{\underset{1}{\cancel{2}}\cdot \underset{1}{\cancel{2}}\cdot \underset{1}{\cancel{3}}\cdot \underset{1}{\cancel{3}}\cdot 3} = \frac{8}{3} \quad \text{or} \quad 2\frac{2}{3}$$

(3) We may change the improper fractions to mixed numbers and proceed to multiply as follows: In the example $\frac{9}{4} \times \frac{32}{27}$

$= ?$ change the $\frac{9}{4}$ to $2\frac{1}{4}$ and the $\frac{32}{27}$ to $1\frac{5}{27}$. Then $2\frac{1}{4} \times 1\frac{5}{27} = ?$ Multiply 2×1 to obtain 2. Multiply $\frac{1}{4} \times \frac{5}{27}$ to obtain $\frac{5}{108}$. Multiply $2 \times \frac{5}{27}$ to obtain $\frac{10}{27}$. Multiply $1 \times \frac{1}{4}$ to obtain $\frac{1}{4}$. Now add 2, $\frac{5}{108}$, $\frac{10}{27}$, and $\frac{1}{4}$, or

$$2 + \frac{5}{108} + \frac{10}{27} + \frac{1}{4} = 2 + \frac{5 + 40 + 27}{108} = 2 + \frac{72}{108} = 2\frac{2}{3}$$

Conversely, mixed numbers may be changed to improper fractions before multiplying, and the operation goes forward as already illustrated. Thus:

$$6\frac{3}{4} \times 1\frac{13}{15} = \frac{\overset{9}{\cancel{27}}}{\underset{1}{\cancel{4}}} \times \frac{\overset{7}{\cancel{28}}}{\underset{5}{\cancel{15}}} = \frac{63}{5} = 12\frac{3}{5}$$

EXERCISE 6

Multiply:

1. $\frac{5}{4} \times \frac{7}{3} =$
2. $\frac{9}{8} + \frac{17}{4} =$
3. $\frac{16}{5} \times \frac{15}{4} =$
4. $\frac{18}{7} \times \frac{14}{3} =$
5. $6\frac{3}{5} \times 18\frac{3}{7} =$
6. $15\frac{3}{4} \times 3\frac{5}{6} =$
7. $83\frac{3}{7} \times 91\frac{4}{5} =$
8. $127\frac{5}{8} \times 234\frac{4}{7} =$
9. $\frac{7}{4} \times \frac{9}{8} \times \frac{5}{2} =$
10. $\frac{14}{5} \times \frac{16}{3} \times \frac{32}{21} =$
11. $\frac{19}{16} \times \frac{32}{5} \times \frac{65}{38} =$
12. $\frac{65}{43} \times \frac{129}{13} \times \frac{69}{18} =$
13. $\frac{8}{3} \times \frac{15}{4} \times \frac{62}{5} \times \frac{95}{4} =$
14. $\frac{124}{35} \times \frac{65}{42} \times \frac{98}{37} \times \frac{74}{49} =$
15. $25\frac{3}{4} \times \frac{6}{5} \times 21\frac{5}{7} =$
16. $42\frac{5}{7} \times \frac{125}{3} \times \frac{8024}{5} =$
17. $\frac{6287}{424} \times \frac{784}{257} \times \frac{93}{67} =$
18. $457\frac{3}{4} \times 62\frac{4}{7} \times \frac{140}{37} =$
19. $\frac{572}{14} \times \frac{56}{21} \times \frac{25}{3} \times \frac{43}{16} \times \frac{142}{37} \times \frac{48}{19} =$
20. $\frac{18}{35} \times \frac{65}{15} \times \frac{6258}{40} \times \frac{91}{13} =$

21. A cubic foot of water weighs $62\frac{1}{2}$ pounds. How much do $5\frac{3}{8}$ cubic feet of water weigh?

22. If a jet plane can fly 600 miles in 1 hour, how far can it fly in $2\frac{3}{5}$ hours?

23. If a city block is $\frac{1}{6}$ mile long, how many miles has a man gone when he has walked $5\frac{1}{4}$ blocks south and $8\frac{1}{2}$ blocks east? If he is trying to walk 5 miles during the day, how many miles does he still lack?

24. If water weighs $62\frac{1}{2}$ pounds per cubic foot, what is the weight of the water in a tank which contains $18\frac{2}{3}$ cubic feet?

25. A recipe reads as follows: 3 cups of flour, 4 teaspoons of baking powder, $\frac{3}{4}$ teaspoon of salt, $2\frac{1}{2}$ tablespoons of sugar, $1\frac{1}{4}$ cups of milk, and $\frac{2}{3}$ cup of shortening. How much of each ingredient will be required to make $3\frac{1}{2}$ times the recipe?

26. If $1\frac{2}{3}$ yards of material is required to make an apron, how many yards are needed to make 5 aprons? If $9\frac{1}{2}$ yards of material were purchased, how much was left over after making 5 aprons?

27. Mortar for 1000 bricks requires $\frac{5}{8}$ cubic yard of sand and $1\frac{1}{8}$ barrels of lime. If the estimate on a building project calls for 8250 bricks, how much sand and lime should be ordered?

28. The circumference of a circle is approximately $3\frac{1}{7}$ times the diameter. Find the circumference if the diameter is $6\frac{3}{4}$ inches.

29. A farmer estimates that it requires around $2\frac{3}{4}$ bushels of seed wheat per acre. How much seed wheat will be needed for $163\frac{3}{8}$ acres?

30. A cookie recipe requires $1\frac{3}{4}$ cups of sugar. How much sugar will be needed to make $3\frac{1}{2}$ times the recipe?

31. If gains on cattle in feed lot amount to $3\frac{1}{4}$ pounds per day per head, in how many days will a steer put on 65 pounds?

32. If it takes approximately $3\frac{4}{5}$ pounds of feed for one dozen eggs, how many eggs may be produced from 456 pounds of feed?

6. DIVIDING IMPROPER FRACTIONS AND MIXED NUMBERS

In dividing two improper fractions we invert the divisor and then multiply the two fractions. For example:

$$\frac{8}{5} \div \frac{56}{15} = \frac{\overset{1}{\cancel{8}}}{\underset{1}{\cancel{5}}} \times \frac{\overset{3}{\cancel{15}}}{\underset{7}{\cancel{56}}} = \frac{3}{7}$$

Here we have $^{56}/_{15}$ as the divisor. Upon inverting $^{56}/_{15}$, we obtain $^{15}/_{56}$. The division process might also be expressed as

$$\frac{\frac{6}{5}}{\frac{126}{25}} = \frac{\overset{1}{\cancel{6}}}{\underset{1}{\cancel{5}}} \times \frac{\overset{5}{\cancel{25}}}{\underset{21}{\cancel{126}}} = \frac{5}{21}$$

In a series of divisions of fractions, such as $4/3 \div 9/8 \div 3/2$, we have

$$4/3 \times 8/9 \times 2/3 = 64/81$$

The easiest way to handle the division of mixed numbers is to change them to improper fractions and proceed as just shown in the dividing of improper fractions. For example:

$$17\tfrac{4}{13} \div 6\tfrac{2}{65} = \frac{225}{13} \div \frac{392}{65} = \frac{\overset{5}{\cancel{225}}}{\underset{1}{\cancel{13}}} \times \frac{\overset{5}{\cancel{65}}}{\underset{8}{\cancel{392}}} = \frac{25}{8} = 3\tfrac{1}{8}$$

EXERCISE 7

Divide as indicated:

1. $9/5 \div 3/2 =$

2. $36/7 \div 9/7 =$

3. $\dfrac{124/9}{44/27} =$

4. $\dfrac{729/124}{243/31} =$

5. $8\tfrac{3}{5} \div 3\tfrac{11}{25} =$

6. $12\tfrac{4}{7} \div 7\tfrac{9}{49} =$

7. $135\tfrac{3}{4} \div 26\tfrac{11}{104} =$

8. $5432\tfrac{3}{8} \div 226\tfrac{67}{192} =$

9. $\dfrac{\frac{8,324}{43}}{\frac{24,972}{817}} =$

10. $\dfrac{\frac{5,746}{89}}{\frac{22,984}{1,157}} =$

11. $\dfrac{\frac{82,463}{127}}{\frac{494,778}{2,159}} =$

12. $\dfrac{6}{5} \div \dfrac{48}{25} \div \dfrac{135}{64} =$

13. $\dfrac{121}{15} \div \dfrac{154}{75} \div \dfrac{143}{56} =$

14. $\dfrac{4624}{27} \div \dfrac{18496}{243} \div \dfrac{81}{32} =$

15. $\frac{17}{8} \div \frac{85}{64} \div \frac{128}{125} \div \frac{1000}{256} =$

16. $\frac{75}{14} \div \frac{375}{84} \div \frac{1296}{625} \div \frac{875}{648} =$

17. $39\frac{3}{4} \div \frac{795}{424} \div \frac{848}{625} =$

18. $197\frac{2}{5} \div \frac{81}{40} \div \frac{328}{243} =$

19. $2564\frac{3}{8} \div 60\frac{4}{7} \div \frac{625}{124} \div \frac{279}{25} =$

20. $43{,}642\frac{3}{17} \div 967\frac{3}{5} \div \frac{243}{68} \div \frac{1428}{729} =$

Perform the indicated operations.

21. $\frac{3}{4} \times \frac{2}{9} \div \frac{7}{15}$
22. $\frac{15}{16} \times \frac{8}{3} \div 7\frac{3}{4}$
23. $\frac{18}{25} \div \frac{3}{5} \times \frac{7}{8}$
24. $\frac{169}{4} \times 3\frac{1}{13} \div \frac{19}{4}$
25. $\frac{225}{14} \div 6\frac{1}{4} \times \frac{7}{15}$

26. A man drives 418 miles in $8\frac{1}{4}$ hours. What is the average speed of the car in miles per hour?

27. A piece of metal $7\frac{3}{4}$ feet in length is to be divided into 8 equal pieces. What will be the length of each piece if it is necessary to allow one-eighth inch for each cut?

28. If a car uses $\frac{3}{22}$ of a gallon of gasoline per mile, how many gallons will be required for a trip of 846 miles?

29. How many pieces $3\frac{5}{16}$ inches in length can be cut from a steel bar $25\frac{1}{4}$ inches in length, if one-eighth inch is allowed for each cut?

30. The diameter of a circle is approximately the circumference divided by $3\frac{1}{7}$. Find the diameter if the circumference is $17\frac{3}{4}$ feet.

31. In the blueprint of a house the architect represented 1 foot by three-eighths inch. If a room measures 12 inches by $6\frac{3}{8}$ inches on the drawing, what are the dimensions of the room?

32. A steam pipe is to be covered with asbestos. If each piece of the asbestos is $3\frac{3}{4}$ feet long, how many pieces are needed to cover a pipe $63\frac{3}{4}$ feet long?

33. How many planks $1\frac{5}{11}$ feet long must be laid end to end to make a row 48 feet long?

34. How many pieces of wire each $4\frac{1}{8}$ feet long can be cut from a coil of wire 156 feet long?

35. The diameter of a circle is approximately the circumference divided by $3\frac{1}{7}$. Find the diameter if the circumference is $14\frac{14}{21}$ feet.

EXERCISE 8
REVIEW

Add:

1. $\frac{1}{2} + \frac{2}{3} + \frac{3}{5} + \frac{4}{9} + \frac{3}{22} =$

2. $\frac{3}{10} + \frac{3}{4} + \frac{5}{16} + \frac{8}{21} + \frac{9}{25} =$

Subtract:

3. $\frac{8}{19} - \frac{2}{5} =$

Multiply:

4. $\frac{3}{5} \times \frac{4}{7} \times \frac{2}{3} =$

5. $\frac{16}{25} \times \frac{3}{5} \times \frac{3}{4} \times \frac{5}{9} =$

6. $\frac{18}{37} \times \frac{74}{108} \times \frac{14}{27} \times \frac{3}{7} =$

Divide:

7. $\frac{5}{6} \div \frac{5}{8} =$

8. $\frac{7}{18} \div \frac{21}{40} =$

9. $\frac{25}{42} \div \frac{5}{7} =$

Add:

10. $5\frac{2}{7} + 3\frac{3}{4} =$

11. $21\frac{2}{3} + 16\frac{3}{4} + 104\frac{16}{19} =$

Subtract:

12. $65\frac{7}{8} - 24\frac{2}{3} =$

13. $102\frac{5}{16} - 28\frac{3}{7} =$

Multiply:

14. $\frac{15}{7} \times \frac{49}{5} \times \frac{14}{9} =$

15. $\frac{16}{3} \times \frac{21}{20} \times \frac{25}{6} =$

16. $15\frac{1}{2} \times 6\frac{2}{3} \times 18\frac{3}{4} =$

17. $125\frac{3}{4} \times 64\frac{3}{8} \times 25\frac{1}{4} =$

Divide:

18. $85/13 \div 340/39 =$ 19. $125/14 \div 15/42 =$

20. $64\frac{2}{3} \div 16\frac{3}{4} =$

21. Mary bought a sheet of postage stamps (100) and used three-fourths of them the first week. How many did she have left?

22. Farmer Smith planted $\frac{2}{3}$ of a 12-acre field in corn. How many acres of corn did he plant?

23. If potatoes are four-fifths water, how much water is there in 5 bushels? (Assume a bushel of potatoes weighs 60 pounds.)

24. Tom reads 300 words a minute and Tack reads four-fifths as many. How many words a minute does Tack read?

25. 500 feet is an increase of $\frac{3}{5}$ over ___?___ feet?

26. A cost-price formula requires the cost of manufacture to be two-thirds less than the selling price. Find the selling price if the cost is $2.

27. On a certain line of goods the net price is one-fourth less than the list price. If the net price of an article is $2.60, what is its list price?

28. A 5-pound roast lost one-fourth of its weight in cooking. How much did it weigh after cooking?

29. If, on the plan of a house which the Joneses are studying, $\frac{1}{8}$ inch represents 1 foot, what are the dimensions of a room which measures $1\frac{1}{4}$ inches by $1\frac{5}{8}$ inches on the plan?

30. A share in the catch of the J. A. Fishing Schooner is one-sixtieth of the value of the catch (after certain fixed charges are met). Slim's allotment is $3\frac{4}{5}$ shares. To what part of the value of the catch is Slim entitled?

31. Jane worked $2\frac{1}{2}$ hours last night on her story for the school paper. Today she finished it in $1\frac{1}{4}$ hours. How long did it take Jane to write the story?

32. A lifeboat carries 7 gallons of water. Eight persons are in the lifeboat. What part of a gallon of water should each be allowed?

33. Can you divide 7 dollar bills among 8 men so that each gets 1 dollar?

34. A box contains 8 apples. Can you divide these among 8 boys, in such a way as to leave 1 apple in the box? (None of the apples should be cut.)

35. Ray's Hamburger Stand buys ground beef in 60-pound lots. If $2/9$ of a pound of ground beef goes into each of Ray's hamburgers, how many hamburgers can he sell from 60 pounds of ground beef?

36. What must 5 be divided by to yield a quotient of $7\frac{3}{5}$?

37. If vegetables, when dried, lose $9/14$ of their fresh weight, how much will $84\frac{3}{4}$ pounds of fresh vegetables weigh when dried?

38. A man paid $143 for a ring, which included the price of the ring and a tax of one-tenth of this price. What was the price of the ring before taxes?

39. A 1–2–4 concrete mixture means 1 part cement, 2 parts sand, and 4 parts gravel. What fractional part of the total mixture is gravel?

40. Cheryl buys a piece of luggage for $44. This price includes the cost of the luggage and a tax of one-tenth of this cost. What was the price of the luggage before the tax was added?

CHAPTER FOUR

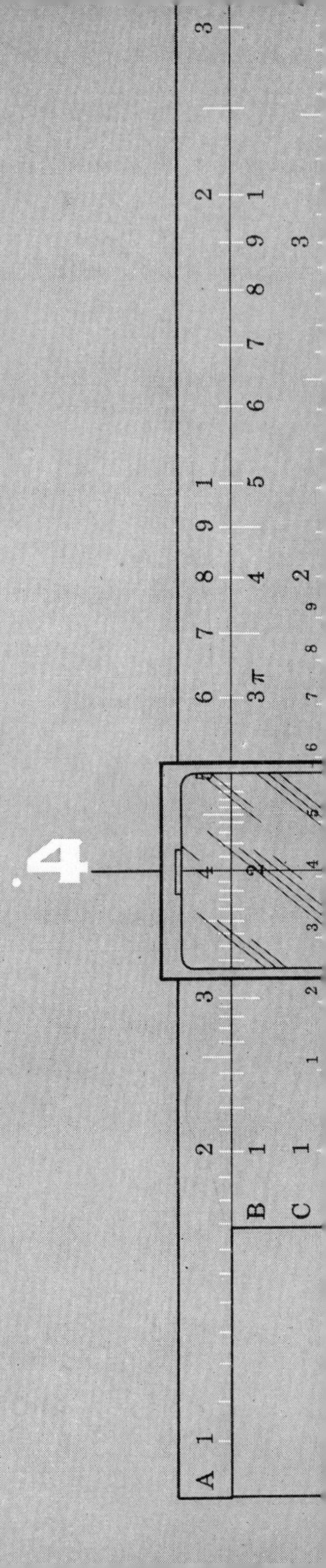

DECIMALS

1. EXTENSION OF PLACE VALUE—DECIMALS

As we observed in Chapter Two, the notation for the natural numbers 0, 1, 2, 3, 4, 5, 6, 7, 8, 9, is also called the *decimal system* (from the Latin *decem,* meaning ten) because ten symbols or digits are used to represent all numbers.

We have already discussed the fact that the place value given to a digit depends on the place the digit occupies relative to the units place. We have illustrated this fact with examples in which the digits were to the left of the units place and in the units place. Thus 5943 means $5(1000) + 9(100) + 4(10) + 3(1)$ or $5(10)^3 + 9(10)^2 + 4(10)^1 + 3(10)^0$.

Let us place a period or dot (.), called the *decimal point,* at the right of the units place and explain place value as it operates at the right of the decimal point. A digit written immediately to the right of the decimal point has a place value which is one-tenth of the place value the digit would have if it stood in the units place.

Let us refer to Figure 2 in which the digit 6, appearing immediately to the right of the decimal point, represents six-*tenths,* or $\frac{6}{10}$. A digit in this position is described as being in the *tenths place.* A digit immediately to the right of the tenths place has a place value equal to one-tenth of the place value the digit would have if it were in the tenths place or one-hundredth of the place value it would have if it were in the units place. In Figure 2, the digit 5 appearing in the second place to the right of the decimal point stands for five *one-hundredths,* or $\frac{5}{100}$. A digit in this position is described as being in the *hundredths place.*

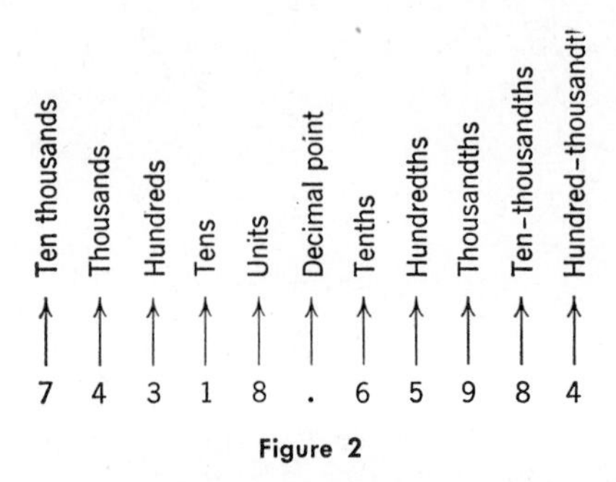

Figure 2

In accordance with the principle of place value, the place value of a digit (both to the left and to the right of the decimal point) is 10 times the place value which that digit would have if it stood in the next place to the right. Digits on the right of the decimal point in a number stand for the number of tenths, hundredths, thousandths, and so forth, which appear in the number. We read the number 74318.65984 in Figure 2 as "seventy-four thousand, three hundred eighteen *and* sixty-five thousand, nine hundred eighty-four hundred-thousandths." In reading a decimal number, the word "and" is used only for the decimal point. Further examples are:

6.7 is read "six and seven-tenths"

18.03 is read "eighteen and three-hundredths"

4634.232 is read "four thousand six hundred thirty-four and two hundred thirty-two-thousandths."

Decimal places refer to the places held by digits in a decimal to the right of the decimal point. Thus 63.75 has two decimal places and 124.687 has three decimal places.

A number which has digits other than zero to the right of the decimal point is called a decimal. Thus 643.29 and 0.831 are decimals. Let us observe that the part of a decimal to the left of the decimal point represents an integer or whole number. Let us examine the part of a decimal to the right of the decimal point.

It is observed to be a proper fraction whose denominator is some power of 10. This fraction is also called a decimal fraction. Thus $0.7 = \frac{7}{10}$, $0.07 = \frac{7}{100}$, $0.073 = \frac{73}{1000}$ are all proper fractions whose denominator is some power of 10. $\frac{7}{10}$ means the same thing as $\frac{7}{10^1}$, $\frac{7}{100}$ means the same thing as $\frac{7}{10^2}$, and $\frac{73}{1000}$ has the same value as $\frac{73}{10^3}$. Now let us reconsider the decimal referred to in Figure 2, namely, 74318.65984. It may be rewritten as

$$7(10{,}000) + 4(1000) + 3(100) + 1(10) + 8(1)$$
$$+ 6\left(\frac{1}{10}\right) + 5\left(\frac{1}{100}\right) + 9\left(\frac{1}{1000}\right) + 8\left(\frac{1}{10{,}000}\right) + 4\left(\frac{1}{100{,}000}\right)$$

This example shows again the positional nature of the decimal system which we treated to some extent in Chapter Two, "Whole Numbers."

2. ADDING AND SUBTRACTING DECIMAL FRACTIONS

We have already observed in connection with the addition and subtraction of whole numbers that only items of the same kind can be added and subtracted. It does not seem unreasonable therefore for us to say that tenths must be combined with tenths, hundredths with hundredths, thousandths with thousandths, and so forth, in adding and subtracting decimals. It is important in both adding and subtracting decimals to keep the decimal points in a line, as well as to have all units (and likewise all tens, hundreds, tenths, hundredths, thousandths, and so forth) in a separate column.

For example add:

```
284.76
 78.928
 64.09
 12.715
-------
440.493
```

Here we have units, tens, and hundreds in individual columns as well as tenths, hundredths, and thousandths.

Starting the addition with the extreme right-hand column and working to the left by columns, we obtain the following results, *in terms of place value.*

$$8/1000 + 5/1000 = 13/1000 = 10/1000 + 3/1000 = 1/100 + \boxed{3/1000}$$

$$1/100 + 6/100 + 2/100 + 9/100 + 1/100 = 19/100 = 10/100 + 9/100$$
$$= 1/10 + \boxed{9/100}$$

$$1/10 + 7/10 + 9/10 + 0/10 + 7/10 = 24/10 = 20/10 + 4/10 = 2 + \boxed{4/10}$$

$$2 + 4 + 8 + 4 + 2 = 20 = 2(10) + \boxed{0(1)}$$

$$2(10) + 8(10) + 7(10) + 6(10) + 1(10) = 24(10)$$
$$= 20(10) + 4(10) = 2(100) + \boxed{4(10)}$$

$$2(100) + 2(100) = \boxed{4(100)}$$

The entire answer can be diagrammed as:

$4(100) + 4(10) + 0(1) + 4(0.1) + 9(0.01) + 3(0.001)$, or
$4(10^2) + 4(10^1) + 0(10^0) + 4(10^{-1}) + 9(10^{-2}) + 3(10^{-3})$.

An example in subtraction follows:

$$\begin{array}{r} 6547.34 \\ 168.274 \\ \hline 6379.066 \end{array}$$

Here the borrowing of the powers of 10 is similar to the carrying procedure just given for addition.

Common fractions may be converted to decimal fractions by dividing the denominator into the numerator. Thus the fraction $\frac{3}{8}$ becomes the decimal fraction 0.375, when we divide the 8 into the 3, and the fraction $\frac{5}{4}$ becomes the decimal fraction 1.25 when we divide the 4 into the 5. Other examples of converting common fractions into decimal fractions are: $\frac{3}{5} = 0.6$, $\frac{5}{16} = 0.3125$, $\frac{7}{4} = 1.75$, and $\frac{9}{5} = 1.8$.

Decimal fractions likewise may be changed into common fractions. For example, 0.125 means $\frac{125}{1000}$ which reduces to $\frac{1}{8}$;

$0.04 = \frac{4}{100} = \frac{1}{25}$; $2.6 = 2\frac{6}{10} = 2\frac{3}{5} = \frac{13}{5}$; $7.125 = 7\frac{125}{1000} = 7\frac{1}{8}$ $= \frac{57}{8}$; and $8.5 = 8\frac{5}{10} = 8\frac{1}{2} = \frac{17}{2}$.

EXERCISE 1

Add the following, and check by casting out nines.

1.
```
  589.62
   27.249
 1643.387
 4398.573
28439.2
    0.0054
 9379.721
```

2.
```
 8137.999
   48.36
    9.238
  268.478
 9947.89
12368.9734
  949.005
```

3.
```
 7842.39
  657.778
 4392.6493
   83.206
  987.3457
53699.9999
 2007.0098
 6700.4309
```

4.
```
30000.009
  402.3697
 6739.8744
88888.7777
 5739.2169
40809.0305
 9754.55593
```

Subtract the following, and check by casting out nines

5.
```
4753.895
 207.006
```

6.
```
28596.3074
 9987.658
```

7.
```
6999.8834
 707.7098
```

8.
```
7647.864
 259.986
```

Write the following numbers in words.

9. 547.62
10. 389.88
11. 9763.774
12. 8755.859
13. 12,587.6794
14. 439,643.9803
15. 673,504.8073
16. 804,367.7405
17. 5,807,669.75934
18. 34,648,992.88739

Express the following in numbers.

19. Eight thousand, six hundred twenty-four and seventy-five-hundredths

20. Four thousand, nine hundred twenty-seven and forty-three-hundredths

21. Sixty-five thousand, seven hundred fifty-nine and four hundred eighty-three-thousandths

22. Ninety-five thousand, four hundred thirty-six and seven hundred thirty-eight-thousandths

23. Six hundred seventy-five thousand, two hundred forty-three and eight thousand seven hundred twenty-six-ten thousandths

24. Nine hundred eighty-seven thousand, six hundred thirty-nine and five thousand four hundred seven-ten thousandths

25. Three million, five hundred sixty-two thousand, seven hundred sixty-three and forty-eight thousand nine hundred sixty-five-hundred thousandths

26. Two hundred forty-five million, eight hundred seventy-five thousand, four hundred fifty-seven and ninety-seven thousand five hundred forty-eight-hundred thousandths

Add the following:

27. 34.68 + 652.389 + 4739.488 + 602.003

28. 253.99 + 7859.067 + 9006.3897 + 47.53

29. 80,752.6503 + 38.47 + 639.7709 + 432,007.97634 + 0.4773 + 9875.268

30. 382,567.025 + 14,803.5974 + 31.27934 + 629.477 + 9489.6308

31. At the beginning of the accounting period for a certain month, the Sims family checking account has a balance of $264.38. During this accounting period the following deposits are made: $601.26, $25.32, $147.83, and $235.67. Checks for the following amounts are written: $10.23, $143.92, $18.43, $69.82, $29.66, $14.53, $35.42, $66.59, $8.59, $42.73, $125.34, $38.66, $38.66, $126.81, $4.03, $29.43, $239.67, $53.02, and $67.23. Find the balance in the account at the close of the accounting period.

32. Mrs. Green has a "charge-a-plate" at a department store.

During a certain month she charges items for the following amounts: \$4.32, \$16.85, \$3.48, \$136.45, \$83.72, \$21.38, \$13.98, \$47.63, and \$108.59. At the beginning of the month she already owed \$12.53. During the month she makes four payments of one hundred dollars each. How does her account stand at the end of the month?

33. The utilities in the LaFonda Apartment run as follows for 12 months: \$483.25, \$452.63, \$563.87, \$749.75, \$679.67, \$588.78, \$544.82, \$472.38, \$495.87, \$462.77, \$410.72, and \$463.47. Find the total for the year.

34. Farmer Brown has the following acreages planted in corn: 8.2, 15.7, 21.5, 15.4, and 12.6. Find the total of his acreage in corn. If the farm contained 152 acres, how many acres are left for uses other than corn?

35. Alvin goes 10 miles per day, Jerry 12, Jose 16, Dave 24, and Elvis 30. They all start together June 1, in going around a circular island in the same direction, 56 miles around. When will they all meet?

Add:

36. $42 + 0.038 + 1.76 + 0.007 + 18.402 =$

37. $0.62 + 784 + 0.378 + 62 + 0.09 =$

Subtract:

38. $859 - 0.642 =$

39. $1437 - 0.053 =$

40. $21 - 0.876 =$

41. $546 - 0.302 =$

Change the following to decimal fractions.

42. $\frac{1}{2}$, $\frac{3}{4}$, $\frac{5}{8}$, $\frac{3}{16}$, and $\frac{5}{32}$

43. $\frac{4}{5}$, $\frac{9}{10}$, $\frac{7}{8}$, $\frac{9}{16}$, and $\frac{3}{15}$

44. $\frac{5}{2}$, $\frac{7}{4}$, $\frac{7}{5}$, $\frac{15}{2}$, and $\frac{17}{8}$

45. $\frac{6}{4}$, $\frac{9}{8}$, $\frac{19}{4}$, $\frac{26}{5}$, and $\frac{25}{8}$

Change the following decimal fractions to common fractions.

46. 0.3125, 0.555, 0.6, 0.16, and 0.0025

47. 0.36, 0.425, 0.625, 0.96, and 0.0625

48. 2.5, 7.8, 9.125, 3.0625, and 25.875

49. 1.2, 45.35, 16.625, 21.375, and 140.25

3. MULTIPLYING DECIMAL FRACTIONS

Multiplication of decimal fractions is carried on in a manner similar to that used with whole numbers and described in Chapter Two. When we multiply 47.63 by 32.57 we line the numbers up with hundredths under hundredths, tenths under tenths, units under units, tens under tens, and hundreds under hundreds. Again it is important to observe place value.

Thus:

$$\begin{array}{r} 47.63 \\ \times\ 32.57 \\ \hline \end{array} \quad \text{is equal to} \quad \begin{array}{r} 47.63 \\ \times\ 0.07 \\ \hline 3.3341 \end{array} + \begin{array}{r} 47.63 \\ \times\ 0.50 \\ \hline 23.8150 \end{array} + \begin{array}{r} 47.63 \\ \times\ 2.00 \\ \hline 95.2600 \end{array} + \begin{array}{r} 47.63 \\ \times\ 30.00 \\ \hline 1428.9000 \end{array}$$

Hence we have:

$$\begin{array}{r} 47.63 \\ \times\ 32.57 \\ \hline 3.3341 \\ 23.8150 \\ 95.2600 \\ 1428.9000 \\ \hline 1551.3091 \end{array}$$

In each of the separate products, 47.63×0.07, 47.63×0.50, 47.63×2.00, 47.63×30.00, we are multiplying hundredths by hundredths, which gives ten-thousandths. Each time, consequently, we point off four places. For example:

$$0.23 \times 0.15 = \frac{23}{100} \times \frac{15}{100} = \frac{23 \times 15}{100 \times 100} = \frac{345}{10000} = 0.0345$$

A simple rule for multiplying decimal fractions is to take the sum of the number of decimal places in the multiplier, and the number of decimal places in the multiplicand and point off this number of decimal places in the product. Thus, in the example 0.23×0.15 we take the sum of two decimal places in the multiplier and two decimal places in the product, and obtain a total of four decimal places. We point off four decimal places in the product, and we have 0.0345.

EXERCISE 2

Multiply the following:

1. 27.54 × 38.6

2. 75.39 × 34.7

3. 898.49 × 56.78

4. 947.63 × 49.37

5. 908.99 × 766.88

6. 754.39 × 872.68

7. 2647.893 × 842.72

8. 4739.763 × 943.82

9. 1004.829 × 87348.657

10. 2059.037 × 92580.264

11. Check problems 1 and 2 by casting out nines.
12. Check problems 3 and 4 by casting out nines.
13. Check problems 5 and 6 by casting out nines.
14. Check problems 7 and 8 by casting out nines.
15. Check problems 9 and 10 by casting out nines.
16. Write in words the product resulting in problem 6.
17. Write in words the product resulting in problem 7.
18. Write in words the product resulting in problem 8.
19. Write in words the multiplier and the multiplicand in problem 9.
20. Write in words the multiplier and the multiplicand in problem 10.
21. The board of directors of an airline is faced with providing money for 38 new jet planes. It finds that the cost of these jets is $5,943,200 each. How much money will need to be secured to finance this purchase?

22. If runways cost $1135.50 a foot, how much will it cost to build 57.9 miles of new runways for jet planes? (There are 5280 feet in a mile.)

23. The manager of Belk Clothing Store finds that if he buys 130 suits the price will be $45.60 each, whereas if he buys 230 suits the price will be $38.40 each. How much additional money is needed by the manager if he purchases 230 suits rather than 130 suits?

24. A food purchase at Breen Bros. Grocery includes the following items: 5 pounds of rump roast at $1.03 per pound; 4 pounds of center cut ham at $1.43 per pound; 8 pounds of hamburger at 87 cents per pound. Canned goods are included as follows: eight cans at 2 for 43 cents; 5 cans at 27 cents per can; 6 cans at 2 for 57 cents; and 5 cans at 47 cents per can. The grocery clerk was given 3 ten-dollar bills. How much change did the customer receive?

25. A rectangular field is 318.24 feet long and 704.87 feet wide. Find the total distance around the field.

26. Mr. Jowers buys 152 bushels of sweet potatoes at $1.27 per bushel and sells them at $2.56 per bushel. Find his profit on the whole transaction.

27. The Fair Trade Market buys 142 dressed hens at 37 cents per pound and sells them at 49 cents per pound. Find the profit on the entire transaction.

28. At $253 per acre, what is the total cost of five tracts of land which contain respectively 6.7 acres, 14.3 acres, 21.7 acres, 2.4 acres, and 17.5 acres.

29. Find the total cost of: 25 pounds of sugar at $0.12 per pound, 6 dozen oranges at $0.32 per dozen and 2 pounds of coffee at $1.08 per pound.

30. Mr. King receives $0.971 per hour for 37.6 hours per week. Mr. Lee receives $1.130 per hour for 25.3 hours per week. Which man earns more per week? How much more does he earn than the other worker?

4. DIVIDING DECIMAL FRACTIONS

Division of decimal fractions is handled in a way similar to that used in Chapter Two with whole numbers. When we divide 6.25 by 2.5, we have $2.5\,\overline{)6.25}$. We recall that the 2.5 is called the divisor and the 6.25 is called the dividend. In dividing decimal fractions we proceed to transform the divisor into a whole number by multiplying it by 10, or 100, or 1000, or whatever power of 10 it takes to change the divisor into a whole number. By a power of 10 we recall that 10^2 means 10×10, or 100, 10^3 means $10 \times 10 \times 10$, or 1000, 10^4 means $10 \times 10 \times 10 \times 10$, or 10,000, etc. In the present illustration, we observe

```
        2.5
2.5. / 6.2.5
  ↗      ↗
       50
       ---
       125
       125
       ---
```

that if we multiply the divisor, 2.5, by 10, we obtain the whole number 25. We also multiply the dividend or 6.25 by 10, obtaining 62.5. Now immediately place the decimal point in the answer (quotient) directly above its new position in the dividend. Division here is carried out in the same manner as division of integers. Upon dividing 25 into 62.5, we obtain 2.5 as the quotient. Let us notice here that when we multiply both the numerator and denominator of a fraction by the same number we do not change the value of the fraction. Thus $2/5$ becomes $4/10$ when both numerator and denominator are multiplied by 2. Two-fifths becomes $6/15$ when both numerator and denominator are multiplied by 3. And $2/5$ becomes $20/50$ when both numerator and denominator are multiplied by 10. Each of the fractions $4/10$, $6/15$, and $20/50$ can be reduced to $2/5$ by dividing both numerator and denominator by the appropriate number. Thus in $4/10$, when both numerator and denominator are divided by 2, we have $2/5$; in $6/15$, when both numerator and denominator are divided by 3, we have $2/5$; in $20/50$, when both numerator and denominator are divided by 10, we have $2/5$.

Again referring back to the illustration $2.5 \overline{)6.25}$, or $\frac{6.25}{2.5}$, or $\frac{62.5}{25}$, we see that 25 divides into 62 two times but not three times, and the answer apparently falls between 2 and 3. As we have just recently shown, the answer is 2.5.

Discussion of approximate numbers will appear in a later chapter. However, in the present chapter we shall set up a partial procedure for the "rounding" of numbers. For example, "round" 87.688, 87.684, 87.685, and 87.675 to two decimal places each. If the digit to be "rounded" is followed by a digit greater than 5, we add one to the digit to be "rounded." Thus, 87.688 becomes 87.69. If the digit to be "rounded" is followed by a digit less than 5, we leave the digit to be "rounded" unchanged. Thus, 87.684 becomes 87.68. If the digit to be "rounded" is even and is followed by a 5, we leave the digit to be "rounded" unchanged. Then 87.685 becomes 87.68. If the digit to be "rounded" is odd and is followed by a 5, we add one to the digit to be "rounded." Thus, 87.675 becomes 87.68. Let us follow these practices as we work with the division of decimal fractions in this chapter. For example:

```
                 19.835
82.47. / 1635.79.462
          8247
          ------
          81109
          74223
          ------
           68864
           65976
           ------
            28886
            24741
            ------
             41452
             41235
             ------
```

Dividing 1635.79462 by 82.47, carrying the result to three decimal places, and then "rounding" to two decimal places, we obtain 19.84.

EXERCISE 3

Round each of the following to two decimal places.

1. 65.378
2. 824.542
3. 579.684
4. 407.746

Round each of the following to three decimal places.

5. 804.6953
6. 1275.8347
7. 4007.8965
8. 3598.6642

In problems 9 through 20, divide, carry the result to three decimal places, and "round" to two decimal places unless the division "comes out even" before the third decimal place is reached.

9. $2.56 \overline{)4.35983}$
10. $35.7 \overline{)65.8394}$
11. $6.668 \overline{)463.896376}$
12. $0.8365 \overline{)15.8627546}$
13. $63.62 \overline{)564.62583}$
14. $3.7 \overline{)0.7568}$
15. $0.62 \overline{)0.08354}$
16. $0.073 \overline{)0.007539}$
17. $83.754 \overline{)25{,}673.462698}$
18. $6.4567 \overline{)1359.875388}$
19. $0.00374 \overline{)0.00386218}$
20. $0.0697 \overline{)0.2658521}$

21. The unit of electric energy is the watt. A 75-watt light bulb consumes 75 watt-hours of electricity in 1 hour. A kilowatt-hour (kwh) is equal to 1000 watt-hours. The Lion's Club rents a church recreation hall for a "fun night." The club agrees to pay $14 plus the cost of the lights. In the recreation hall there are eighty-two 150-watt light bulbs and forty-eight 200-watt bulbs. What is the rental if the club will require the use of the gymnasium for 5 hours and 45 minutes, and electric energy costs 4.5 cents per kwh?

22. The Brown Beaver Scout Troop collects 1632 pounds of scrap paper which they sell for 83 cents per 100 pounds. What do they receive for the paper?

23. The J. and S. Feed Store buys a carload of wheat for $42.00 a ton and sells it for $1.73 a bushel. If the wheat weighs 8640 pounds, what profit does the feed store realize? (Assume 1 bushel wheat = 60 pounds.)

24. A farmer sells 183 bushels of wheat at $1.43 per bushel and takes his pay in flour at 6.75 cents per pound. How many 100-pound sacks of flour does he receive?

25. The manager of Baker and Sons exchanges 342 yards of silk purchased at $1.92 per yard for percale at 13.8 cents per yard. How many yards of percale does he receive?

26. A ship sails 320 nautical miles. A nautical mile is 1.15 land or statute miles. How many statute miles does the ship sail?

27. How much must be paid for 135 feet of steel bar weighing 1.73 pounds per foot and costing $7.43 per hundred pounds?

28. A metal alloy used to make bearings for certain machinery is 0.75 copper, 0.14 tin, and 0.11 zinc. How many pounds of each metal are in 142 pounds of alloy?

29. If 1 quart of paint will cover 238 square feet, how many quarts will be needed to cover 9 walls, each 22 feet long and 8 feet high? Give the answer to the nearest quart.

30. A knot is a nautical mile per hour. A ship has a speed of 42 miles per hour. What is its speed in knots? Refer to problem 26.

31. How can 10 plums be placed in 3 cups so that every cup will contain an odd number of plums?

CHAPTER FIVE

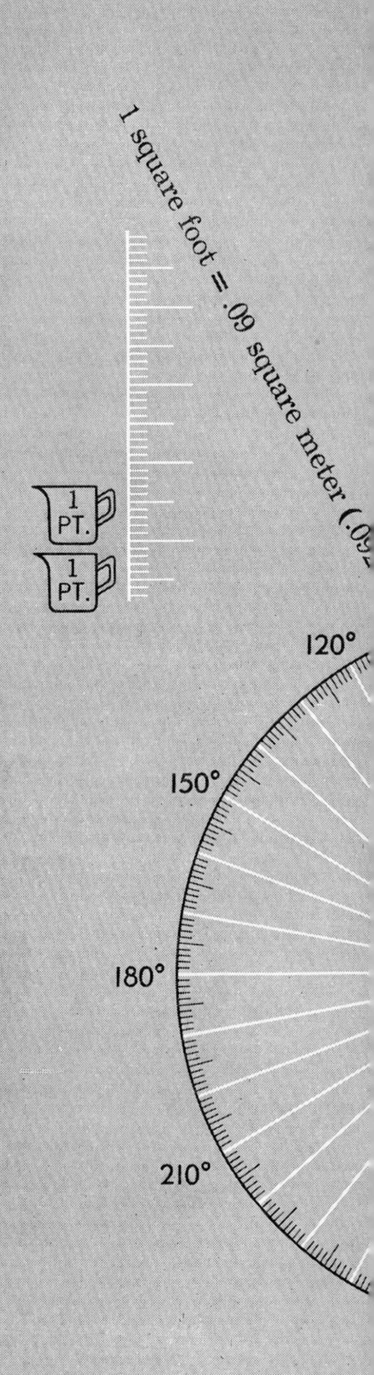

WEIGHTS AND MEASURES

1. NATIONAL SYSTEM OF WEIGHTS AND MEASURES

The history of our units of measure is quite interesting. Some of these units were of natural origin. The length of the foot was, to begin with, the actual length of the human foot. It varied from $9\frac{3}{4}$ inches to 19 inches at different times according to English history. It is said that Henry I, who lived in the twelfth century, proclaimed that the lawful yard was the distance from the end of his nose to the end of his thumb when his arm was outstretched horizontally. The mile was originated by the Romans. They used it as the length of 1000 double paces where the pace was approximately $2\frac{1}{2}$ feet long. Henry VIII in the sixteenth century set up the weight of the pound as the weight of 7000 grains of wheat taken from the middle of the ear and well dried. The early units of measure were indefinite and variable and led to considerable confusion. They were, of course, a handicap in setting up trade agreements between various countries. As civilization moved forward it was necessary to adopt standard units of measure.

The standard unit of measure needs to be rigidly defined in terms of some unchanging element of nature in order that the unit may be rebuilt in various localities. In 1826, it was decided in England that the imperial yard would be $\frac{360,000}{391,393}$ of the length of a seconds pendulum at sea level in the latitude of London. After a great deal of work, the length was determined, and the standard yard was placed in the House of Parliament. Of course errors were made in the measurements. Also the standard was destroyed when the House of Parliament burned in 1834. The Astronomical Society had made a copy of the standard and it became the basis for the English imperial yard which is now defined as the distance between two scratches on a special metal rod at a given temperature.

The French government undertook to develop an ideal unit of length early in the nineteenth century. They defined the meter to be $\frac{1}{10,000,000}$ of the distance from one pole of the earth to the equator. This was determined after a very extensive survey and the standard meter was set up. However, errors were made in the calculations and actually the meter has no special relation to the length of the earth's quadrant. Instead, the standard meter is a completely arbitrary and artificial length defined as the distance at the temperature of melting ice between the centers of two lines etched on the platinum iridium bar deposited at the International Bureau of Weights and Measures, Paris, France.

After a standard unit of length has been derived, the standard units of weight and volume can be expressed in terms of this unit of length. The English troy pound, for instance, equals the weight of 22.778 cubic inches of water at 4° C. The United States gallon is the equivalent of 231 cubic inches. The gram, which is the basic unit of weight in the metric system, equals the weight of one cubic centimeter of distilled water at 4° C.

The United States Bureau of Standards in Washington has a copy of the standard meter, and Congress has defined the fundamental units of our national system of weights and measures in terms of this standard meter. For example, Congress has said that the national yard shall be equal to $\frac{3600}{3937}$ of a meter, or 39.37 inches long. In the case of the English yard, a meter is equal to 39.370113 inches. Thus our national yard is slightly longer than the English imperial yard. There are some other differences between the measures used in England and the United States.

Listed here are the common measures used in the United States for length, area, volume, and capacity.

LENGTH

12 inches = 1foot
3 feet = 1 yard
16½ feet, 5½ yards = 1 rod
5280 feet, 1760 yards, 320 rods = 1 mile

AREA

144 square inches = 1 square foot
9 square feet = 1 square yard
30¼ square yards = 1 square rod
160 square rods = 1 acre
640 acres = 1 square mile

VOLUME

1728 cubic inches = 1 cubic foot
27 cubic feet = 1 cubic yard

DRY MEASURE

2 pints = 1 quart
8 quarts = 1 peck
4 pecks = 1 bushel
1 bushel = 2150.42 cubic inches

LIQUID MEASURE

2 gills = 1 cup
2 cups = 1 pint
2 pints = 1 quart
4 quarts = 1 gallon
1 gallon = 231 cubic inches
31½ gallons = 1 barrel
2 barrels = 1 hogshead

AVOIRDUPOIS WEIGHT

7000 grains, 16 ounces = 1 pound
100 pounds = 1 hundredweight
2000 pounds = 1 ton
2240 pounds = 1 long ton

APOTHECARIES' WEIGHT

20 grains = 1 scruple
3 scruples = 1 dram
8 drams = 1 ounce
12 ounces, 5760 grains = 1 pound

APOTHECARIES' LIQUID

60 minims = 1 fluid dram
8 fluid drams = 1 fluid ounce
16 fluid ounces = 1 pint
8 pints = 1 gallon

TIME

60 seconds = 1 minute
60 minutes = 1 hour
24 hours = 1 day
7 days = 1 week
52 weeks = 1 year
365 days = 1 common year
366 days = 1 leap year
360 days = 1 commercial year
10 years = 1 decade
100 years = 1 century

SURVEYORS' LENGTH

7.92 inches = 1 link
25 links = 1 rod
4 rods = 1 chain
80 chains = 1 mile

SURVEYORS' AREA

625 square links = 1 square rod
16 square rods = 1 square chain
10 square chains = 1 acre
640 acres = 1 section
36 sections = 1 township

PAPER

24 sheets = 1 quire
20 quires = 1 ream
2 reams = 1 bundle
5 bundles = 1 bale
500 sheets = 1 ream

MISCELLANEOUS

1 acre = 40 yards x 120 yards, approximately
1 carat = 200 milligrams
1 cord = 128 cubic feet
1 hand = 4 inches
1 furlong = 40 rods
1 cubic foot = about 7½ gallons
1 knot = 1.15 miles per hour

Avoirdupois weight is commonly used for weighing objects. The long ton is used at times where coal and other products of the mine are involved.

For example, find the number of reams of paper in 1 bale of paper. We find in the table that 2 reams = 1 bundle and 5 bundles = 1 bale. Consequently, 10 reams = 1 bale.

As another example, find the number of acres in 10 sections of land. In the table we find that 1 section equals 640 acres. Ten sections equal 10 times 640 acres or 6400 acres.

EXERCISE 1

1. Find the number of square feet there are in an acre.
2. Change 18 feet 5 inches to inches.
3. Change 23 feet 7 inches to inches.
4. Change 7 gallons 3 quarts to pints.
5. Change 16 gallons 5 quarts to pints.
6. Change 8 pounds 4 ounces to ounces.
7. Change 15 pounds 6 ounces to ounces.
8. Change 7 miles 49½ feet to rods.
9. Change 11 miles 858 feet to rods.
10. Change 15 bushels 2 pecks to quarts.
11. Change 23 bushels 3 pecks to quarts.
12. Change 2½ gallons to cups.
13. Change 5¾ gallons to cups.
14. Change 3 acres to square feet.
15. Change 7 acres to square feet.
16. Change 5607 square feet to square yards.
17. Change 23,436 square feet to square yards.
18. Change 162 ounces to pounds and ounces.
19. Change 257 ounces to pounds and ounces.
20. Change 639 inches to feet and inches.
21. Change 416 inches to feet and inches.
22. Change 324 pints to gallons.
23. Change 147 pints to gallons.
24. Change 246 pints to quarts.
25. Change 542 pints to quarts.
26. Change 432 cubic feet to cubic yards.
27. Change 68,418 cubic feet to cubic yards.
28. Change 1956 feet to rods and feet.
29. Change 2348 feet to rods and feet.
30. Change 151 quarts to bushels, pecks, and quarts.
31. Change 238 quarts to bushels, pecks, and quarts.
32. Change 6492 pounds to tons and pounds.
33. Change 8764 pounds to tons and pounds.

34. Add 15 quarts 1 pint, 23 quarts 1 pint, 17 quarts 1 pint, 39 quarts 1 pint, and 39 quarts 1 pint.

35. Add 73 quarts 1 pint, 25 quarts 1 pint, 29 quarts 1 pint, 61 quarts 1 pint, 38 quarts 1 pint, and 47 quarts 1 pint.

36. Add 35 pounds 6 ounces, 12 pounds 9 ounces, 78 pounds 5 ounces, 62 pounds 7 ounces, and 82 pounds 9 ounces.

37. Add 124 pounds 8 ounces, 87 pounds 8 ounces, 15 pounds 14 ounces, 43 pounds 7 ounces, and 83 pounds 15 ounces.

38. Add 5 gallons 1 pint, 9 gallons 4 pints, 7 gallons 6 pints, 3 gallons 3 pints, 25 gallons 2 pints, and 11 gallons 9 pints.

39. Add 69 gallons 3 pints, 14 gallons 7 pints, 42 gallons 5 pints, 12 gallons 4 pints, and 51 gallons 9 pints.

40. Add 5 hours 20 minutes 8 seconds, 12 hours 35 minutes 22 seconds, 6 hours 15 minutes 19 seconds, 36 hours 42 minutes, and 16 hours 51 minutes 28 seconds.

41. Add 14 hours 45 minutes 9 seconds, 32 hours 15 minutes 18 seconds, 62 hours 28 minutes 15 seconds, 17 hours 25 minutes 112 seconds, and 45 hours 16 minutes 29 seconds.

42. Subtract 14 pounds 13 ounces from 25 pounds.

43. Subtract 19 pounds 12 ounces from 53 pounds 5 ounces.

44. Subtract 43 feet 9 inches from 64 feet 6 inches.

45. Subtract 27 feet 7 inches from 53 feet 6 inches.

46. Subtract 7 hours 36 minutes from 19 hours 52 minutes.

47. Subtract 12 hours 42 minutes from 17 hours 15 minutes.

48. Subtract 6 gallons 3 quarts 1 pint from 25 gallons 2 quarts 2 pints.

49. Subtract 15 gallons 2 quarts 1 pint from 63 gallons.

50. Multiply 7 feet 5 inches by 25.

51. Multiply 6 feet 10 inches by 36.

52. Multiply 15 pounds 9 ounces by 37.

53. Multiply 27 pounds 14 ounces by 82.

54. Multiply 23 hours 42 minutes by 19.

55. Multiply 42 hours 17 minutes by 64.

56. Multiply 23 feet 8 inches by 15 feet 4 inches.

57. Multiply 175 feet 7 inches by 36 feet 5 inches.

58. Multiply 83 feet 15 inches by 47 feet 18 inches.

59. Multiply 267 feet 19 inches by 634 feet 23 inches.

60. Divide 64 pounds 12 ounces by 4.

61. Divide 132 pounds 13 ounces by 5.

62. Divide 26 hours 45 minutes by 5.

63. Divide 140 hours 42 minutes by 8.

64. Divide 23 feet 8 inches by 5 feet 4 inches.

65. Divide 264 feet 9 inches by 6 feet 3 inches.

66. Divide 68 pounds 3 ounces by 2 pounds 5 ounces.

67. Divide 242 pounds 8 ounces by 30 pounds 2 ounces.

68. If $46\frac{1}{2}$ quarts of milk weigh 100 pounds, find the weight of 5 gallons of milk. (Round answer to nearest whole number of pounds.)

69. Find the cost of 2 pounds 14 ounces of sirloin steak at $1.04 per pound.

70. Twelve clerks in The Franks Department Store worked the following number of hours during one week: 44 hours 35 minutes, 40 hours, 46 hours 40 minutes, 42 hours 45 minutes, 48 hours 20 minutes, 30 hours 15 minutes, 50 hours 55 minutes, 45 hours 10 minutes, 52 hours 40 minutes, 47 hours 55 minutes, 35 hours 15 minutes, and 52 hours 20 minutes. What was the average number of hours worked by the twelve clerks?

71. Each delegate to a firemen's convention is to be provided with a badge to be made from a 6-inch piece of ribbon. At 44 cents a yard, what is the total cost of the ribbon if 1260 delegates are expected?

72. A child weighed 7 pounds 3 ounces at birth. A year later she weighed 15 pounds 2 ounces. How much weight did the child gain in one year? What was the per cent of increase?

73. Johnny sold 8 hens weighing 7 pounds 3 ounces, 6 pounds 9 ounces, 6 pounds 5 ounces, 7 pounds 8 ounces, 5 pounds 6 ounces, 6 pounds 6 ounces, 4 pounds 10 ounces, and 5 pounds 14 ounces. Find the average weight of the hens.

74. How much did Johnny receive if the hens brought 41 cents per pound?

75. A fuse contains $2\frac{1}{2}$ ounces of black powder. How many fuses can be made from 250 pounds of powder?

76. When a car is traveling 60 miles per hour, how many feet does it go in 1 second?

77. Two pieces of wire 15 feet 7 inches and 13 feet 9 inches, respectively, are cut from a length of wire 50 feet long. How long is the remaining piece?

78. Change 750,000 seconds to weeks, days, hours, minutes, and seconds.

79. A wheel makes 1260 revolutions per minute. How many revolutions does it make in 1 second?

80. An English examination consists of three parts which are to be taken in succession with no break. The first part runs for 12 minutes, the second 21 minutes, and the third 18 minutes. If the examination begins at 10:00 A.M. when will it end?

81. Mr. Stone has employment other than his regular job. He works 2 hours 15 minutes on Monday, 3 hours 20 minutes on Tuesday, 1 hour 45 minutes on Wednesday, 2 hours 40 minutes on Thursday, and 4 hours 15 minutes on Friday. If this additional work pays him $4.00 per hour, how much extra does Mr. Stone earn during the week?

82. How many square feet are there in 126 square yards?

83. If each one of 25 children at Lakeview School drinks one-half pint of milk every day at school for 16 weeks, how many gallons of milk will they use?

84. A sanding machine motor makes 48 revolutions per second. How many revolutions does it make per minute?

85. How many revolutions will the motor in the above problem make in two-thirds of a minute?

86. How many revolutions will the motor in problem 84 make in three-fourths of an hour?

87. How many revolutions will the motor in problem 84 make in 5 hours?

88. Ethyl gasoline is made by adding a liquid called tetraethyl lead to ordinary gasoline. One gallon of tetraethyl is needed for every 1200 gallons of gasoline. A pint of tetraethyl lead will be enough for how many gallons of gasoline?

89. If a drill will cut through steel plate $\frac{1}{2}$ inch thick in 60 revolutions, under the same conditions how many revolutions will it take to drill through a steel plate $3\frac{1}{4}$ inches thick?

90. Have some fun discovering a person's age and month of birth. Ask the person whose age you are trying to discover to do the writing. Suppose John is 18 and that he was born in September. Let John write as follows without letting you see the computations:

Number of month of birth	9
Multiply by 2	18
Add 5	23
Multiply by 50	1150
Add John's age, 18	1168
Subtract 365, obtaining	803
Add 115	918

John finds the result, 918. He can now be told that his age is 18, and September, or the ninth month, is the month of his birth. The two figures on the right in the result, 918, give the age. The remaining figure or figures give the month in which the birthday comes.

91. How many squares of tile 6 inches by 6 inches would it take to cover a rectangular floor 14 feet by 12 feet?

2. METRIC SYSTEM OF WEIGHTS AND MEASURES

The basic units in the metric system are the meter, gram, and liter. As we have already observed, the meter is the distance between two marks on a platinum bar which is kept in Paris. More specifically it is equal approximately to 39.37 inches.

A gram is one-thousandth of a certain piece of platinum which is also kept in Paris. It takes approximately 28.35 grams to equal 1 ounce.

The liter equals 1000 cubic centimeters. Approximately 3.785 liters equal 1 gallon.

The metric system has 10 as its base, and names of the units other than meter, gram, and liter are found by adding prefixes to the names meter, gram, and liter.

These prefixes are: milli- = one-thousandth; centi- = one-hundredth; deci- = one-tenth; deka- = ten; hecto- = one hundred; and kilo- = one thousand. Thus one millimeter equals one-thousandth of a meter, one centimeter equals one-hundredth of a meter, and one kilometer equals one thousand meters.

Let us consider the following tables for metric measures of length, weight, and capacity.

LENGTH MEASURE

Standard unit, 1 meter (or 1 m)

1 millimeter (mm) = 0.001 m
1 centimeter (cm) = 0.01 m
1 kilometer (km) = 1000 m

WEIGHT MEASURE

Standard unit, 1 gram (or 1 g)

1 milligram (mg) = 0.001 g
1 centigram (cg) = 0.01 g
1 kilogram (kg) = 1000 g

CAPACITY MEASURE

Standard unit, 1 liter (or 1 l)

1 milliliter (ml) = 0.001 l
1 centiliter (cl) = 0.01 l
1 kiloliter (kl) = 1000 l

We see that 10 centimeters = 1 decimeter, and 10 decimeters = 1 meter. Also 10 meters = 1 dekameter, 10 dekameters = 1 hectometer, and 10 hectometers = 1 kilometer.

Likewise 10 centigrams = 1 decigram, 10 decigrams = 1 gram, 10 grams = 1 dekagram, 10 dekagrams = 1 hectogram, and 10 hectograms = 1 kilogram.

We find considerable debate concerning the relative merits of the metric and national systems of weights and measures. Only the United States and Great Britain have not adopted the metric system. Scientists everywhere use the metric system.

For example, how many grams are there in 3 kilograms? Since, from the table, 1 kilogram = 1000 grams, 3 kilograms = 3000 grams.

As another example, find the number of centimeters in a kilometer. We know that 100 centimeters equal 1 meter, and 1000 meters equal one kilometer. Therefore 100 × 1000 or 100,000 centimeters equal one kilometer.

EXERCISE 2

1. How many millimeters are there in one meter?
2. How many millimeters are there in one kilometer?
3. How many centimeters are there in 300 millimeters?
4. How many millimeters are there in 40 centimeters?
5. How many grams are there in 5000 milligrams?
6. How many milligrams are there in 0.03 gram?
7. How many centigrams are there in one kilogram?
8. How many kilograms are there in 300 milligrams?
9. How many centimeters are there in 175 meters?
10. How many meters are there in 450 centimeters?
11. How many milliliters are there in 50 liters?
12. How many milliliters are there in 50 centiliters?
13. Convert 2,325,469 centimeters to kilometers, meters, and centimeters.
14. Subtract 14 centimeters 5 millimeters from 1 meter.
15. Find one-third of 15 meters 5 decimeters 20 centimeters.
16. How many grams are there in three kilograms?
17. How many kilograms are there in 600 grams?
18. How many grams are there in 3600 milligrams?
19. How many centigrams are there in 40 grams?
20. How many milligrams are there in 75 grams?
21. How many grams are there in 4.75 kilograms?
22. How many kilograms are there in 700 grams?
23. How many kilometers are there in 356 meters?
24. How many centimeters are there in 4800 meters?
25. How many centiliters are there in 25 liters?
26. How far apart are the longest divisions on a meter stick?
27. What metric unit would you use in taking the dimensions of your classroom?
28. What change in the position of the decimal point do we make in changing meters to kilometers?
29. What metric unit would it be best to use in measuring the distance from Los Angeles to Chicago?

30. What change in the position of the decimal point do we make in changing from kilograms to grams?

31. Reduce 123 kilometers 342 meters to kilometers.

32. The distance from Cologne to Coblenz is 91,000 meters. Change this to kilometers.

33. Change 5438 square millimeters to square centimeters.

34. The edge of a cube is 50 centimeters long. How many decimeters is this?

35. Ice is 0.92 as heavy as water. Find the weight in kilograms of 1.5 cubic meters of ice. A cubic meter of water weighs 1 metric ton. One metric ton weighs 1000 kilograms.

36. A schoolroom in Switzerland is 9 meters long, 8.3 meters wide and 4.1 meters high. How many pupils may use this room if 10.5 cubic meters of air are allowed for each pupil?

37. A line is 80 millimeters long. How many centimeters long is it?

38. What part of a meter is 80 millimeters?

39. Change 0.45 square meters to square centimeters.

40. A metric ton is equal to how many grams?

3. EXPONENTS AND SCIENTIFIC NOTATION

Many numbers in astronomy, chemistry, and physics are either very large or very small. Furthermore, these numbers are generally approximate numbers, with three, four, or five significant digits available. Ordinarily they are used in working out three or four digit answers. Exponents together with decimals are used to represent these quantities. We shall discuss decimals and approximate numbers in later chapters, but we would like to introduce the idea of an *exponent* at this point, and show how it is used in the representation of very large and very small dimensions and quantities.

The following examples show a few powers of 10 in terms of *exponents.*

$100{,}000 = 10 \times 10 \times 10 \times 10 \times 10 = 10^5$, read "ten to the fifth."

$10{,}000 = 10 \times 10 \times 10 \times 10 = 10^4$, read "ten to the fourth."

$1000 = 10 \times 10 \times 10 = 10^3$. read "ten to the third" or "ten cubed."

$100 = 10 \times 10 = 10^2$, read "ten squared."

$10 = 10^1$, read "ten to the first power" or simply "ten." Usually when we have a number raised to the first power we *omit* the 1.

$1 = 10^0$, read "ten to the zero power." This is a *definition,* consistent with the other powers.

$$0.1 = \frac{1}{10} = 10^{-1}, \text{ read "ten to the minus one."}$$

$$0.01 = \frac{1}{100} = \frac{1}{10 \times 10} = \frac{1}{10^2} = 10^{-2}, \text{ read "ten to the minus}$$
two."

$$0.001 = \frac{1}{1000} = \frac{1}{10 \times 10 \times 10} = \frac{1}{10^3} = 10^{-3}, \text{ "ten to the}$$
minus three."

$$0.0001 = \frac{1}{10{,}000} = \frac{1}{10 \times 10 \times 10 \times 10} = \frac{1}{10^4} = 10^{-4}, \text{ "ten to}$$
the minus four."

$$0.00001 = \frac{1}{100{,}000} = \frac{1}{10 \times 10 \times 10 \times 10 \times 10} = \frac{1}{10^5} = 10^{-5},$$
"ten to the minus five."

We may multiply powers of ten by adding the exponents (algebraically), and we may divide powers by subtracting exponents.

Thus: $10^5 \times 10^3 = 10^8$

$(100{,}000)(1000) = 100{,}000{,}000$

And: $10^4 \times 10^{-3} = 10^1 = 10$

or, $10{,}000 \times \dfrac{1}{1000} = 10$

Furthermore: $10^3 \times 10^{-5} = 10^{-2} = 0.01$

$$1000 \times \frac{1}{100{,}000} = \frac{1}{100} = 0.01$$

Consider the distance to the sun. This distance is about 93,000,000 miles. We may write this number in the following ways:

$93{,}000{,}000 = 93 \times 10^6 = 930 \times 10^5 = 9.3 \times 10^7$.

The last of these forms using exponents, namely, 9.3×10^7, is called the *Scientific Notation* for the number 93,000,000. Notice that the number 9.3 in the expression 9.3×10^7, is a number between 1 and 10. The scientific notation follows the practice of writing any number as a number between 1 and 10, multiplied by the appropriate power of 10. The term scientific notation is used because this form for writing numbers is widely followed in scientific work.

Thus: $93{,}000{,}000 = 9.3 \times 10^7$

The velocity of light is an important quantity in the universe. This velocity is about 186,000 miles per second. The number 186,000 may be expressed as follows:

$186{,}000 = 186 \times 10^3 = 18.6 \times 10^4 = 1.86 \times 10^5.$

The last of these, or 1.86×10^5, is the scientific notation for 186,000. Again, 1.86 is a number between 1 and 10.

Suppose we wish to know how long it takes light to travel from the sun to the earth. The time is found by dividing the distance by the rate.

Then: $$\text{time} = \frac{93 \times 10^6 \text{ miles}}{186 \times 10^3 \text{ miles/sec.}}$$

$$= \frac{93 \times 10 \times 10 \times 10 \times 10 \times 10 \times 10}{186 \times 10 \times 10 \times 10} \text{ seconds}$$

$$= \frac{93 \times 10 \times 10 \times 10}{186} \text{ seconds}$$ (dividing both numerator and denominator by 10^3).

$$= \frac{1}{2} \times 10^3 \text{ seconds} = 500 \text{ seconds}$$ after dividing both numerator and denominator by 93.

A more simple solution would be

$$\text{time} = \frac{9.3 \times 10^7}{1.86 \times 10^5} = 5 \times 10^2 = 500 \text{ seconds}$$

This last solution is based on the scientific notation.

The preceding examples illustrate that exponents are numbers, written at the upper right of a quantity, telling how many times the quantity is used in a given product, as a factor. Thus 5^3 means $5 \times 5 \times 5$ or 125, and 4^2 means 4×4, or 16. We refer to the quantity which is used as a factor here as the *base,* and we often refer to the exponent as a power of the base. Thus in 5^3, 5 is the base, 3 is the exponent or power, and we say that 5 is raised to the third power.

A number itself, such as 7, could be written 7^1, but as a matter of convention we omit the 1.

It is necessary to agree on what we mean by "0" or zero as an exponent. By *definition,* any number (except zero) raised to the zero power, such as 7^0 or 10^0, is equal to 1. This definition is consistent with our other work in exponents. Thus we find:

$$10^3 \times 10^2 = (10 \times 10 \times 10)(10 \times 10) = 10^5$$

We *add exponents* when we multiply. And:

$$10^4 \times 10^0 = 10^{4+0} = 10^4$$

This means that when we multiply by 10^0 we get back what we had originally which is the same as multiplying by 1. That is:

$$10^4 \times (10^0) = 10^4, \text{ and } 10^4(1) = 10^4$$

Hence it is consistent to make $10^0 = 1$.

Very small numbers require *negative* exponents to express them. Thus 1 millimeter, which is commonly used in scientific measurement $= \frac{1}{1000}$ meter $= \frac{1}{10 \times 10 \times 10}$ meter $= \frac{1}{10^3}$ meter. By *definition* again, we say that $\frac{1}{10^3} = 10^{-3}$, and $\frac{1}{10^6} = 10^{-6}$. Decimals can also be used for these numbers. Thus $\frac{1}{1000} = 0.001$, hence $10^{-3} = 0.001$, and likewise $10^{-6} = 0.000001$.

Consider the radius of a hydrogen atom; it is approximately 10^{-8} centimeter, or 0.00000001 centimeter. The radius of the electron is even smaller, about 2×10^{-13} centimeter, or 0.0000000000002 centimeter. Negative exponents can be used advantageously here.

Let us use these ideas in representing numbers. Consider the following examples.

The distance to the moon is 240,000 miles. $240{,}000 = 2.4 \times 10^5$.

The velocity of light is 300,000,000 meters per second, or 3.0×10^8 meters per second.

The number of molecules in a gram-molecular weight of a gas such as oxygen is 602,500,000,000,000,000,000,000, which is much more simply written in the form 6.025×10^{23}.

One millimeter is 0.001 meter or 1 millimeter $= 10^{-3}$ meter.

One micron $= 0.000001$ meter; 1 micron $= 10^{-6}$ meter.

The wavelength of sodium light is 0.00005893 centimeter: $0.00005893 = 5.893 \times 10^{-5}$.

The angstrom unit for measuring wavelengths of light and other radiation is 0.00000001 centimeter, or 1 Å $= 10^{-8}$ centimeter.

EXERCISE 3

1. Change each number from exponent form to standard form.

$3 \times 10^3 = 3000$

$7 \times 10^5 =$

$1.68 \times 10^8 =$

$2.6 \times 10^4 =$

$5 \times 10^{-4} =$

$1.63 \times 10^{-11} =$

$6.3 \times 10^{12} =$

$2 \times 10^{-3} = 2/1000 = 0.002$

$3.2 \times 10^{-2} =$

$1.86 \times 10^{12} =$

$98 \times 10^7 =$

$1.64 \times 10^{-24} =$ (mass of hydrogen atom in grams)

2. Change each number to scientific notation.

$23{,}000 = 2.3 \times 10^4$

$16{,}000{,}000 =$

$93{,}000{,}000 =$

$0.00004 =$

$0.0166 =$

$0.000015 =$

$480{,}000 =$

$2160 =$

$0.0002 = 2 \times 10^{-4}$

$0.000049 =$

$0.000001 =$

$23{,}000{,}000{,}000 =$

3. The following physical constants are given in scientific notation; write them in standard form.

2.998×10^{10} centimeters per second $= c$ (velocity of light).

6.547×10^{-27} c.g.s. units* $= \hbar$ (Planck's constant)

4.77×10^{-10} e.s.u.† $= e$ (charge on the electron)

1.09737×10^5 units $= R$ (Rydberg spectra constant)

1.650×10^{-24} gram $= p$ (mass of the proton)

4. The following astronomical numbers are in standard form. Change them to scientific notation.

---

* The c.g.s. system is the centimeter-gram-second system and is widely used by physicists.

† Electrostatic units.

Diameter of Jupiter, 88,600 miles =
Mean distance from the sun to Jupiter, 483,000,000 miles =
Number of seconds in a year, 31,560,000 =
Number of miles in one light-year, 5,880,000,000,000 =
Distance to the nearest star, 25,300,000,000,000 = (miles)

4. THE BINARY SYSTEM

We have already observed that our *decimal system* is written according to the base 10. Now that electronic digital computers are being rather extensively used, considerable attention is being given to the base two, which formerly appeared largely in theoretical mathematics. Two is the base of the binary system, in which all numbers are represented by the use of the two digits 1 and 0. For example, 11011 is a number written to the base 2. Let us write this number in the base 10. Then:

$$11011 = 1\cdot 2^4 + 1\cdot 2^3 + 0\cdot 2^2 + 1\cdot 2^1 + 1\cdot 2^0 = 16 + 8 + 0 + 2 = 26 \text{ in the base } 10$$

Base 2 can be used in high-speed electronic digital computers because electrical pulses can be sent through vacuum tube circuits at a rate of several million per second, with the presence of a charge at an instant corresponding to "1" and the absence of a charge corresponding to "0". The vacuum tubes or other electronic valves act as gates which either permit charges to pass through a circuit or keep them from passing through a circuit. It is not a difficult engineering problem to design circuits which will add 2 ones and carry, so that $1 + 1 = 10$, which represents 2; similarly, such circuits will add $1 + 10$ to get 11, or 3. It is a fairly difficult job in "logical analysis" or "logical design" to make computer devices which will perform general computing routines efficiently. These machines must be designed so that they will follow coded instructions. Once such machines are designed they do exactly what they are supposed to do, without any errors, as long as the circuits are intact. They can add or subtract, multiply or divide, in a matter of a few millionths of a second.

Thus 1 in the binary system equals 1 in the decimal system.

$$10 \text{ in the binary system} = 1\cdot 2^1 + 0\cdot 1 = 2$$
$$11 \text{ in the binary system} = 1\cdot 2^1 + 1\cdot 1 = 3$$
$$100 \text{ in the binary system} = 1\cdot 2^2 + 0\cdot 2^1 + 0\cdot 1 = 4$$

101 in the binary system $= 1\cdot 2^2 + 0\cdot 2^1 + 1\cdot 1 = 5$
110 in the binary system $= 1\cdot 2^2 + 1\cdot 2^1 + 0\cdot 1 = 6$
111 in the binary system $= 1\cdot 2^2 + 1\cdot 2^1 + 1\cdot 1 = 7$
1000 in the binary system $= 1\cdot 2^3 + 0\cdot 2^2 + 0\cdot 2^1 + 0\cdot 1 = 8$
1001 in the binary system $= 1\cdot 2^3 + 0\cdot 2^2 + 0\cdot 2^1 + 1\cdot 1 = 9$

We see that the sequence of natural numbers 1, 2, 3, 4, 5, 6, 7, 8, and 9, is represented in the binary system as 1, 10, 11, 100, 101, 110, 111, 1000, and 1001.

The number 100011 in the binary system is the same as 35 in the decimal system since

$$1\cdot 2^5 + 0\cdot 2^4 + 0\cdot 2^3 + 0\cdot 2^2 + 1\cdot 2^1 + 1\cdot 2^0 = 35$$

Let us compare this with our natural numbers or numbers to the base 10. Thus:

$$\begin{aligned} 6354 &= 6(1000) + 3(100) + 5(10) + 4(1) \\ &= 6(10)^3 + 3(10)^2 + 5(10)^1 + 4(10)^0 \end{aligned}$$

It is observed that when the base is 10, the 10 is raised to various powers, whereas when the base is 2, the 2 is raised to various powers.

The most convenient method for changing from 35 in the decimal system, or base 10, to the binary system, or base 2, is by successive division.

Thus:

2 / 35
2 / 17 remainder 1
2 / 8 remainder 1
2 / 4 remainder 0
2 / 2 remainder 0
2 / 1 remainder 0
0 remainder 1

Hence, 35 (base 10) = 100011 (base 2).

EXERCISE 4

Write the following natural numbers as numbers with the base 2.

1. 6
2. 14
3. 23
4. 37
5. 46
6. 59
7. 64
8. 78
9. 82

10. 95
11. 103
12. 247
13. 649
14. 2352

The following numbers are written in the binary system. Translate each into the decimal system.

15. 10
16. 100
17. 101
18. 111
19. 1000
20. 1001
21. 1101
22. 1100
23. 1111
24. 10010
25. 11010
26. 111100
27. 100100100
28. 1100111001

5. CONVERSION OF UNITS

In carrying on business transactions with people in Central America, South America and continental Europe for example, we need to be able to convert from United States units to units in the metric system. We also need to know how to convert from units in the metric system to United States units. By United States units we mean the units such as feet, pounds, and gallons.

The following conversion table is convenient.

CONVERSION TABLE

From United States units to Metric System units

1 inch = 2.54 centimeters
1 square yard = 0.836 square meter
1 cubic yard = 0.765 cubic meter
1 pound = 0.454 kilogram
1 quart = 0.946 liter

From Metric System to United States System

1 meter = 39.37 inches
1 square meter = 1.196 square yards
1 cubic meter = 1.308 cubic yards
1 kilogram = 2.205 pounds
1 liter = 1.057 quarts

For example, find the number of square feet in 5 square meters. From the table just presented, 1 square meter = 1.196 square yards. Now 5 square meters = $5 \times 1.196 = 5.980$ square yards. But 1 square yard = 9 square feet; therefore 5.980 square yards = 9×5.980 square feet = 53.82 square feet. We find then that there are 53.82 square feet in 5 square meters.

As another example, find the number of centimeters in 3 yards. Three yards = 108 inches. Therefore the number of centimeters in 3 yards is $108 \times 2.54 = 274$ centimeters.

In the two preceding examples, as well as in the exercises which follow, we assume that the given measure is exact,* and we round the result to the appropriate number of significant figures. The number of significant figures in the answer will depend on the number of significant figures in the conversion table. Thus in the first example, 1 square meter = 1.196 square yards (4 significant figures). In the second example, 1 inch = 2.54 centimeters (3 significant figures). The answer is 274.32 centimeters, or 274 centimeters when rounded to 3 significant figures.

EXERCISE 5

1. Change 15 meters to inches.
2. Change 3 miles to meters.
3. How many meters does a boy run in the 100-yard dash?
4. How many feet are there in 25 meters?
5. Change 16 liters per second into gallons per hour.
6. Change 22,500 meters to miles.
7. Change 7 pounds per minute into grams per second.
8. How many millimeters are there in 3 feet?
9. A car can go 10 kilometers on 2 liters of gasoline. How many miles will it travel on a gallon of gasoline?
10. The 440-yard dash is equivalent to how many meters?
11. Find the number of centimeters in an inch.
12. How many grams equal an ounce?
13. How many square feet are there in a square meter?
14. Change 24 inches to meters.
15. Change 35 feet to meters.
16. Change 434 yards to meters.
17. Change 14 miles to meters.
18. Change 75 feet 8 inches to meters.
19. Change 43.5 meters to feet.
20. Change 5.82 kilometers to feet.

---

* Exact numbers and approximate numbers are treated in more detail in Chapter 7.

21. Change 753 centimeters to feet.

22. Change 93.8 pounds to kilograms.

23. Change 13 ounces to kilograms.

24. Change 460 grams to kilograms.

25. Change 7 pounds 9 ounces to kilograms.

26. Change 75 grams to pounds.

27. Change 7.8 kilograms to pounds.

28. Change 84 ounces to pounds.

29. Change 4.6 liters to cubic inches.

30. The average height of a man is 5 feet 8 inches. Express this height in centimeters.

31. If air pressure is 16.3 pounds per square inch of surface, find the pressure in pounds per square centimeter.

32. The barometric reading is 32.4 inches at a given time. Write this in millimeters.

33. A white rat weighed 372 grams. Find its weight in pounds.

34. A scale for a map is set up so that 1 inch = 15 miles. How many miles would be represented by 60 millimeters?

35. A nautical mile is 6080.27 feet. Convert this to meters.

36. An admiral's gold braid is 2 inches wide. What is its width in centimeters?

37. Two airports are 136 kilometers apart. How many miles is it from one airport to the other?

38. Write in kilometers the distance from Chicago to Minneapolis. Assume this distance is 610 miles.

39. A bag of potatoes weighs 25 pounds. Find its weight in kilograms.

40. The Empire State Building is 1248 feet high. Find its height in kilometers.

EXERCISE 6
REVIEW

1. Add
35.69
4.68
0.27
84.74
7.04

2. Check problem 1 by casting out nines.

3. Find the number of times a clock strikes in a day if it only strikes the hours.

4. Here and there and a half of here and there is what per cent of here and there?

5. Tank A holds 642 gallons of oil. Tank B holds 836 gallons. Compare the capacity of the tanks by showing in decimal form the fractional part that tank A is of tank B.

6. Find 124¼% of $72.

7. Bill sold apples costing $8.40 at a profit of 20% of the cost. How much did he make?

8. A rope 90 feet long shrank 0.7% when wet. How much did it shrink?

9. Divide $27\overline{)4829}$ and check by casting out nines.

10. Write in words $8,423,962,437.

11. Write in words $732,564,859,608.

12. Write 942,000,000 in the scientific notation.

13. Write 63,700,000 in the scientific notation.

14. The diameter of the universe is 6×10^9 light-years. Express this in ordinary notation.

15. A gram of radium gives off 3.7×10^{10} alpha particles per second. Write this in ordinary notation.

16. 128 is a number written in the base 10. Write this number in the base 2.

17. 542 is a number written in the base 10. Write this number in the base 2.

18. 10100 is written in the base 2 or binary system. Write this number in the decimal system.

19. 1000000000 is written in the base 2 or binary system. Write this number in the decimal system.

20. Express the number 5⅔ as the sum of an integer and a proper fraction.

21. Multiply the approximate numbers 8.346 and 7.59.

22. Multiply the approximate numbers 256.57 and 92.4.

23. Divide 95.65 by 3.7. Assume both are approximate numbers.

24. Divide 279.78 by 4.72. Assume both are approximate numbers.

25. Add the approximate numbers: 9.837, 42.68, 0.238, 0.7532.

26. Add the approximate numbers: 34.69, 8.737, 0.69, 2.8306.

27. Noon temperatures on 5 successive days were 88°, 95°, 92°, 86°, and 89°. Find the mean or average temperature. (Add the 5 temperature readings and divide by 5.)

28. The measurements of a room were found to be 15.8 feet long, 10.4 feet wide, and 8.6 feet high. Find the area of the inner surface of the room.

29. Find the volume of the room in problem 28.

30. The specific gravity of a substance equals the weight of a given volume of that substance divided by the weight of an equal volume of water. Find the specific gravity of glass, assuming that glass weighs 167.3 pounds per cubic foot and that a cubic foot of water weighs 62.5 pounds.

31. Find the specific gravity of ice if a cubic foot of the ice weighs 52.7 pounds.

32. The circumference of a circle is found from the relationship $C = \pi d$, in which d is the diameter. If $\pi = 3.14159$ approximately, find the circumference of the circle whose diameter is 5.2 inches.

33. Using the information given in problem 32, find the circumference of the circle whose diameter is 6 miles.

34. Metal parts, each weighing 0.487 pound are produced by a machine. What will 85 of these parts weigh?

35. Find the area of a rectangle of length 124.3 inches and width 8.9 inches.

36. There is approximately 0.4535924277 kilogram in a pound. A man weighs 182.5 pounds. Find his weight in kilograms.

37. Simplify: $\dfrac{\frac{5}{6}}{\frac{1}{2} + \frac{2}{3}}.$

38. Simplify: $\dfrac{\frac{2}{3} + \frac{2}{5}}{\frac{3}{2} + \frac{2}{3}}.$

39. Sixteen is what fraction of 56?

40. Three-eighths is what fractional part of $3/5$?

41. Sam reads 300 words a minute and Pug reads $3/4$ as many. How many words a minute does Pug read?

42. $72 = 3/5$ of ?

43. 126 inches = $3/4$ of ? inches.

44. Last year the enrollment of a college was 3500. This year the report is that it has increased one-tenth. If this is exactly true, what is the enrollment this year?

45. A certain cost-price formula requires the cost of manufacture to be two-thirds less than the selling price. What is the selling price when the cost is $4?

46. Goods are on sale at two-fifths less than regular prices. If an article is on sale for $15, what was its regular price?

47. When the Giants have played 72 games and won 55, what is their standing? That is, what part of their games have they won? Round the answer to three decimal places.

48. Round to two decimal places: 6.487; 3.064; 3.025.

49. Round to two decimal places: 1.472; 0.0782; 9.634.

50. Six is what per cent of 3?

51. 1000% of 25 = ?

52. Write 1918 in the Roman notation.

53. Write 1941 in the Roman notation.

54. Write MCM in our notation.

55. Write MDC in our notation.

56. Ganymede, a satellite of Jupiter, is 664,000 miles from Jupiter. Write this in the scientific notation.

57. Europa, another satellite of Jupiter, is 415,000 miles from Jupiter. Write this in the scientific notation.

58. The force of gravity between the sun and the earth written in dynes is 324×10^{25}. Write this in the ordinary notation.

59. The sun's mass equals 199×10^{31} grams. Write this in the ordinary notation.

60. Write 10000000000, which is according to base 2, as it would appear to the base 10.

CHAPTER SIX

PERCENTAGE

1. DEFINITIONS

Percentage is widely used by the modern business man. Merchants use it in computing markups and discounts, and banks use it in lending and borrowing money. Percentage is also utilized by local, state, and federal agencies when they collect taxes, it is used by insurance companies in determining rates, and it is used by newspapers and magazines in describing such things as business and population changes, accident rates on the highways, and agricultural production. All of us come in contact with it to such an extent that it is very important that we understand clearly what it is and how it is used.

The term *per cent* comes from the Latin *per centum* which means *by the hundred.* Thus, the original meaning of 6 per cent was 6 out of every hundred. The per cent sign (%) came into being in the fifteenth century but was not generally used until many years later. It is interesting that the per cent sign contains two zeros, one for each zero in 100.

The meaning of per cent is now much broader than the original concept of by the hundred. We not only use 6% and 60%, but we also deal with 600% and sometimes even 6000%. According to modern usage, a *per cent* is a fraction having 100 for the denominator.

Percentage is that portion of arithmetic dealing with *per cent.* However, the terms *per cent* and *percentage* are frequently used interchangeably. We shall discuss the meaning of *percentage* further as we proceed in this chapter.

2. REDUCTION OF A PER CENT TO A DECIMAL FRACTION

Since per cent is only another way of saying hundredths, 6% = 6 hundredths = $6/100$ = 0.06. A per cent can be reduced to a decimal fraction by dropping the per cent sign and moving the decimal point two places to the left. For example:

$$8\tfrac{1}{2}\% = 0.08\tfrac{1}{2},\ 250\% = 2.50, \text{ and } 4000\% = 40.00$$

EXERCISE 1

Change the following per cents to decimal fractions.

1. 2%
2. 4%
3. 5½%
4. 7½%
5. 75%
6. 83%
7. 125%
8. 325%
9. 450%
10. 675%
11. 5025%
12. 7063%
13. 52.65%
14. 43.74%
15. 384.5%
16. 792.3%
17. 6027¾%
18. 10,049½%
19. 2547.125%
20. 33,057½%

21. A cut of sirloin steak is described as being 18% bone. Write this per cent as a decimal fraction.

22. The rental on my house is to be increased 12.5%. Write this per cent as a decimal fraction.

23. A student on the business staff of a college paper will receive a commission of 15% on all the advertising space he sells. Write his commission rate as a decimal fraction.

24. 64½% of a college class in mathematics commutes. Write this as a decimal fraction.

3. REDUCTION OF A DECIMAL FRACTION TO A PER CENT

We may write the decimal fraction 0.07 in its equivalent form $7/100$ or 7%, since, as we have recently pointed out, a per cent is a fraction having 100 for the denominator. A convenient rule to follow in changing a decimal fraction to a per cent is *to move the decimal point two places to the right and annex the per cent sign.*

Other examples are: 0.09 = 9%, 0.0825 = 8.25%, and $0.06\frac{1}{4}$ = $6\frac{1}{4}$%.

EXERCISE 2

Change the following decimal fractions to per cents.

1. 0.05	**2.** 0.08
3. 0.0725	**4.** 0.0675
5. $0.09\frac{3}{4}$	**6.** $0.06\frac{4}{5}$
7. 0.8392	**8.** 0.7684
9. 2.473	**10.** 3.568
11. 67.92	**12.** 93.45
13. $753.23\frac{1}{2}$	**14.** $837.34\frac{3}{4}$
15. 0.04758	**16.** 0.06892
17. $64.33\frac{1}{4}$	**18.** $98.57\frac{3}{8}$
19. 473.25	**20.** 829.64

21. Certain kinds of fish lose 0.29 of the original weight in cleaning. Change this decimal fraction to a per cent.

22. Eighteen-carat gold is 0.75 gold while copper and silver combine to make up the remaining 0.25. Change both of these decimal fractions to per cents.

23. From the sum of 62.5%, 0.0345, 6.23, and 45.27% subtract the sum of 0.2362, 8.97%, $42\frac{1}{2}$%, and 0.0643. Express the result in per cent.

24. The single discount rate which is the equivalent of two given successive discount rates is found by multiplying the two given discount rates and subtracting this product from the sum of the two given discount rates. Find the single discount rate which is equivalent to two successive discount rates of 12% and 15%. Express the answer in per cent.*

4. REDUCTION OF A PER CENT TO A COMMON FRACTION

As we have noticed, per cent is another way of saying hundredths. Thus: 5% = 5 hundredths $= \frac{5}{100} = \frac{1}{20}$. The equivalent

* Discounts reduce the price of goods or the amount of a bill or debt and are frequently given to encourage payment before the due date.

common fraction to 5% is $\frac{1}{20}$. Other examples are: $8\% = \frac{8}{100} = \frac{2}{25}$;

$$12\tfrac{1}{2}\% = \frac{12\frac{1}{2}}{100} = \frac{\frac{25}{2}}{100} = \frac{25}{200} = \frac{1}{8}; \text{ and } 62\tfrac{1}{2}\% = \frac{62\frac{1}{2}}{100} = \frac{125}{200} = \frac{5}{8}.$$

These common fractions should always be reduced to lowest terms.

The following per cents reduce to the so-called business fractions which are very commonly used in the business world.

50%	= 1/2	20%	= 1/5
33⅓%	= 1/3	40%	= 2/5
66⅔%	= 2/3	60%	= 3/5
25%	= 1/4	80%	= 4/5
75%	= 3/4	16⅔%	= 1/6
83⅓%	= 5/6	8⅓%	= 1/12
12½%	= 1/8	41⅔%	= 5/12
37½%	= 3/8	6¼%	= 1/16
62½%	= 5/8	5%	= 1/20
87½%	= 7/8	4%	= 1/25

EXERCISE 3

Change the following per cents to common fractions reduced to lowest terms.

1. 7%
2. 9%
3. 25%
4. 35%
5. 125%
6. 150%
7. 3¼%
8. 8⅗%
9. 65.25%
10. 34.63%
11. 525½%
12. 683½%
13. 5255%
14. 6432%
15. 233⅓%
16. 438⅔%
17. 0.7825%
18. 0.6532%
19. 757.65%
20. 824.88%

21. Brock pays 40% of the price of an automobile as a down payment. Write this per cent as a common fraction.

22. Milk tests 4.4% butterfat. Write this per cent as a common fraction.

23. Express 15/100, 15%, and 0.15 as twentieths.

24. Instead of multiplying 72 by $12\frac{1}{2}\%$, what fractional part of 72 should we take? Find $12\frac{1}{2}\%$ of 72.

5. REDUCTION OF A COMMON FRACTION TO A PER CENT

We have already observed that a common fraction is transformed into a decimal fraction by dividing the denominator into the numerator. The decimal fraction is changed to per cent by moving the decimal point two places to the right and annexing the per cent sign. Thus $\frac{4}{5} = 0.80 = 80\%$, and $\frac{15}{2} = 7.50 = 750\%$.

EXERCISE 4

Change the following common fractions to per cents.

1. $\frac{3}{5}$	2. $\frac{3}{4}$	3. $\frac{5}{8}$
4. $\frac{7}{8}$	5. $\frac{17}{4}$	6. $\frac{19}{4}$
7. $\frac{18}{3}$	8. $\frac{20}{2}$	9. $\frac{13}{8}$
10. $\frac{17}{5}$	11. $\frac{300}{400}$	12. $\frac{500}{400}$
13. $\frac{625}{125}$	14. $\frac{636}{106}$	15. $\frac{1500}{5}$
16. $\frac{1800}{6}$	17. $\frac{61}{4}$	18. $\frac{82}{5}$

In problems 19 and 20, carry the division to four decimal places, round to three and then change to per cent.

19. $\frac{85}{95}$ 20. $\frac{123}{45}$

In the following four problems, arrange in order of size, beginning with the smallest:

21. $58\%, \frac{18}{23}, \frac{3}{5}, 0.6\frac{3}{5}$

22. $\frac{4}{3}, 125\%, \frac{3}{4}, 1\frac{1}{8}$

23. $62\frac{1}{2}\%, \frac{3}{8}, \frac{3}{4}, 0.4\frac{3}{4}$

24. $\frac{1}{10}, .25\%, \frac{1}{75}, \frac{19}{24}$

25. Read the following numbers and tell which of them are equal: 3; 300%; $\frac{300}{100}$; 8; 800%; $\frac{150}{50}$.

26. A team won $\frac{5}{8}$ of the games it played. What per cent did it win?

27. The Pi Mu team lost 9 games out of 36 games played. The games lost were what part of the games played? Change this common fraction to a per cent.

6. THE THREE CASES OF PERCENTAGE

What is 25% of 64? To determine this the per cent is first reduced to a decimal fraction, then 25% of 64 = 0.25 of 64 = 0.25 × 64 = 8. In the latter multiplication, the multiplier, 0.25, is called the *rate*, the multiplicand, 64, is the *base*, and the product, 8, is the *percentage*. These three quantities are connected by the relationship

$$Rate \times Base = Percentage$$

If any two of the three quantities are given, the third can be found. Consequently, there are three basic cases of percentage: (1) given the rate and the base, to find the percentage; (2) given the base and the percentage, to find the rate; (3) given the rate and the percentage, to find the base. Let us consider each of these cases.

(1) *Find the percentage.* The problem of finding a per cent of a number is another way of finding a fractional part of the number. In finding a per cent of a given quantity, first reduce the per cent to either a common fraction or a decimal fraction, and multiply.

For example, find $12\frac{1}{2}\%$ of 64.08. Reducing to a common fraction, $12\frac{1}{2}\%$ of 64.08 = $\frac{1}{8}$ of 64.08 = 8.01. Reducing to a decimal fraction, $12\frac{1}{2}\%$ of 64.08 = 0.125 × 64.08 = 8.01. Here, 0.125 is the rate, 64.08 is the base, and 8.01 is the percentage.

(2) *Find the rate.* A rather common problem is to determine the per cent one number is of another. Thus, what per cent of 96 is 24? Here, the base, 96, and the percentage, 24, are given. Now, by the fundamental relationship just given, rate × 96 = 24. This means that the product of two numbers is 24, and that one of the two numbers is 96. Division is defined as the process of finding either of two numbers when their product and the other number are known. From the definition of division, the other number may be found by dividing; then, rate = $\frac{24}{96}$ = 0.25 = 25%.

As another example, find what per cent of 144 is 54. Now, rate × 144 = 54, or rate = $\frac{54}{144}$ = 0.375 = 37.5%.

(3) *Find the base.* To find the base when the rate and percentage are given, reduce the rate either to a common fraction or to a decimal fraction.

For example, a house rents for $1800 per year and the rental represents 10% of the value of the house. Find the value of the house. Now, $0.10 \times \text{base} = \$1800$. Here the product of two numbers and one of the numbers are given. From the definition of division, the other number can be found by dividing. Now, base $= \frac{\$1800}{.10} = \$18{,}000$.

Sometimes it is confusing in percentage questions to determine which type of problem is involved. Try to be careful not to confuse the base and the percentage. Sometimes the percentage or rate may be stated indirectly, and it is necessary to read the problem very carefully.

EXERCISE 5

In any of these exercises if the answers do not come out even they should be rounded to two decimal places.

1. Find 16% of 83.
2. Find 72% of 75.
3. What is 55% of 65?
4. What is 37% of 18?
5. Find 82.6% of 133.
6. Find 63.8% of 465.
7. 25 is what per cent of 625?
8. 16 is what per cent of 64?
9. 432 is what per cent of 654?
10. 216 is what per cent of 420?
11. Seven hundred forty-three and six hundred eighty-five thousandths is what per cent of nine thousand five hundred eighty-four and four thousand six hundred seventy-seven ten thousandths?
12. Five hundred sixty-seven and three hundred seventy-nine thousandths is what per cent of eight thousand three hundred forty-seven and eight thousand four hundred thirty-nine ten thousandths?
13. Find a number such that 33 per cent of it is 66.
14. Find a number such that 14 per cent of it is 42.
15. Find a number such that 48 per cent of it is 92.
16. Find a number such that 62 per cent of it is 135.

17. Thirty-five and ninety-five hundredths is 42 per cent of what number?

18. One hundred forty-six and five hundred sixty-seven thousandths is 75 per cent of what number?

19. Find a number such that 63 per cent of it is 172.8.

20. Find a number such that 48 per cent of it is 168.9.

21. Find a number such that $78\frac{3}{4}$ per cent of it is 672.8.

22. Find a number such that $47\frac{7}{8}$ per cent of it is 369.8.

23. 231.7 is what per cent of 439.7?

24. 8562 is what per cent of 12680?

25. 548 is what per cent of 236?

26. 1269 is what per cent of 564?

27. 642.3 is what per cent of 238.6?

28. 1269 is what per cent of 247.9?

29. 5786 is what per cent of 347.8?

30. 6259 is what per cent of 342.7?

31. Find 126% of 873.

32. Find 183% of 684.

33. Find 342% of 364.

34. Find 689% of 743.

35. Find 234.8% of 672.

36. Find 32.59% of 398.

37. Find a number such that 338.6% of it is 65.

38. Find a number such that 758.3% of it is 347.

39. Find a number such that 483.7% of it is 847.

40. Find a number such that 5627% of it is 648.

41. If 26 per cent of a 1850-pound load of peaches were spoiled, how many pounds of peaches were spoiled?

42. If 74 per cent of the total weight of a hog can be made into edible products, how many pounds of food can be used from a 196-pound hog?

43. Sam's Drive-In buys a box of 24 candy bars for 80 cents and sells them for 5 cents each. What per cent of his sales is profit?

44. An automobile listed at $2480 was sold at a 15% discount. What was the selling price?

45. A chair listed at $89 was sold during a sale for $78. What was the per cent of discount?

46. Mr. Barker with a salary of $6500 a year was given a 10% cut. Later his salary was increased 10%. What was his salary after the increase?

47. Dee is paid a salary of $3000 a year plus a commission of 4% on his sales. What must be the amount of his sales during the year if he wishes to receive a total salary of $9000?

48. A house rents for $1200 per year. If the rent represents 12% of the value of the house, what is the house worth?

49. A merchant failed in business. His assets amounted to $28,342 and his liabilities to $83,592. What per cent of his liabilities did he pay? How much did a creditor receive who was owed $1562?

50. The list price of a mathematics textbook is $6.75, less a discount of 15% to teachers. What is the net price of the book to a teacher?

51. A house is insured for three-fourths of its assessed value of $9800. If the insurance rate is ¼% a year, what is the premium per year?

52. Assuming a fish loses 28% of its weight in cleaning, how many pounds of cleaned fish can be obtained from 950 pounds of raw fish?

53. A concrete mixture is 1 part cement, 2 parts sand, and 2 parts gravel by weight. What per cent of the mixture is cement? Sand? Gravel?

54. In the above problem, how many pounds of cement are in 5 tons of the mixture?

55. According to the data in problem 53, how many pounds of the mixture can be made with 22,000 pounds of gravel?

56. A 4200-pound automobile contains 85 pounds of chromium, 120 pounds of lead, and 462 pounds of rubber. What per cent of its total weight is chromium? Lead? Rubber?

57. Green gold is 60% gold, 35% silver, and 5% copper. How many ounces each of gold, silver and copper are in 3500 ounces of green gold?

58. Duralumin is one-half of 1% magnesium. How many pounds of duralumin can be made with 75 pounds of magnesium?

59. One ton of a commercial feed contains 6 pounds of salt. What per cent of the feed is salt?

60. A man invested $16,500 and lost $320. What per cent of his investment did he lose?

61. Wrought iron is 99.8 per cent pure iron. How many pounds of impurities are in 194.68 tons of wrought iron?

62. Some steel contains three-fourths of 1% of carbon. How many tons of this steel can be made with 2460 pounds of carbon?

63. An aluminum alloy called lynite is used for piston rods in motors. Lynite includes 11% by weight of copper. How many pounds of lynite would contain a total of 620 pounds of copper?

64. A hard silver solder, used for soldering metals where the job must withstand very severe strains, is an alloy including 6.8% by weight of zinc. How many pounds of this alloy will be made by adding 12.3 ounces of zinc to the proper proportions of the other materials?

65. A flock of 50,000 hens on The Fresh Egg Poultry Farm averages 3800 dozen eggs per day. What per cent production is this?

7. ARITHMETIC IN THE BUSINESS WORLD

Let us now consider some basic topics in business arithmetic.

If a storekeeper sells an article for $5 and this article *cost* him $3, we say that he has made a *gross profit* of $2 on the sale. If he decides to sell one of these articles for $1.50, he has had a *loss* of $1.50 on the sale. *Gross profit* is the difference between the *selling price* and the *cost*. *Gross profit* is rarely ever the actual profit made by the merchant. Such expenses as advertising, payrolls, rent, taxes, etc., are not included when the *gross profit* is computed. *Gross profit* is also called markup. *Net profit* is the *actual profit* left over after *all expenses* have been deducted from the *gross profit*. *Gross margin* is another term for *gross profit*. Thus if net sales for a day are $4683 and the cost of goods sold is $2569, then the *gross margin* or *gross profit* is $4683 − $2569 = $2114.

One of the important things a business man needs to understand about his business is the cost of selling his product or his *selling expense*. *Selling expense* includes commissions, salesmen's salaries, etc. The business man needs to know the selling expense per dollar of sales or the ratio of selling expense to sales. For example he may compare the months of March and August. If there is a significant difference between the two months, he might decide to change the size of the sales force.

The *selling expense* per dollar of sales is found by dividing the total sales expense by the total sales. If the total sales for a certain day are $312 and the selling expenses for that day are $40, then the selling expense per dollar of sales is $40 \div 312 = 0.1282$. It costs $0.1282 to sell $1 worth of goods. This result of course needs to be small if the man is to continue his business. In order to compare selling expenses it is frequently necessary to carry this division to several places.

Dollar markup is another frequently used business term. It may be the *per cent markup times the cost,* or it may be the *per cent markup times the selling price,* depending on which is used as the base. Per cent markup times the cost is also known as *profit on cost,* whereas per cent markup times the selling price is referred to as *profit on selling price* or *profit on sales.* Regardless how the dollar markup is arrived at, we always have the basic relationship: "selling price equals cost plus dollar markup."

In the paragraph just above we have used the phrase *profit on cost.* Of course this means that the selling price is arrived at by taking a per cent of the cost. For example, a television set costs a dealer $86.50. At what price should he sell it to have a markup of 40% on the cost? The solution is as follows:

Cost	$86.50
Profit or markup = 40% or 0.40×86.50	34.60
Selling price	$121.10

We have also referred to *profit on selling price.* Although dollar markup can be conveniently calculated when profit is figured on cost, merchants usually make their markups a per cent of the selling price, rather than a per cent of the cost. They are of course using the selling price rather than the cost as a base. Probably the main reason for this procedure is that the sales records tell the merchant much more easily what his sales for the day, week, or month have been than his records can tell him what the costs of certain goods sold were. This information is easily available from the cash register. His other records are generally in reference to his sales. Advertising, rent, salaries, salesmen's commissions, taxes, utilities, and so forth are usually posted as costing a certain per cent of his sales. Since almost every expense is referred to sales it is practical to use the sales figure as the base for the markup.

As an example, a furniture store has an electric refrigerator priced to sell at $620. If the store figures its profit at 45% of the sale price, find the profit.

Solution: 45% of $620 or $0.45 \times 620 = \$279$ profit. This represents gross profit of course and does not include freight, store rent, clerical salaries and so forth.

EXERCISE 6

1. The Prade Store wants to buy some shirts to sell at $4.50. It wishes to show a gross profit of 45% on the selling price. How much may it pay for the shirts?

2. An article costing $10.00 is sold at a markup of 25% on the cost. Find the per cent markup on the selling price.

3. An article costing $18.00 is sold at a markup of 30% on the cost. Find the per cent markup on the selling price.

4. The Cushion Sole Shoe Store wants to buy some shoes to sell at $16.00. It wishes to show a gross profit of 42% on the selling price. How much may it pay for the shoes?

5. Gloves were bought at $36.00 a dozen pair and sold at $4.50 per pair. What was the per cent profit on cost, and what was the per cent profit on selling price?

6. All prices at a fire sale are to be reduced by one-third. What should be the sale price on an article formerly priced at $14.70?

7. How much must a salesman, working on a 15% commission, sell per month to earn $620 a month?

8. A dress is advertised for $25, which represents a 20% reduction from its former price. What was the former price?

9. Membership in a consumers' union entitles a member to a 15% discount on all purchases in certain stores. What will some furniture listed at $382 cost a member if he lives in a state where there is a 3% sales tax?

10. A gas bill of $14.26 may be paid in full within ten days for $13.20. What per cent saving is involved?

11. An employee earning $125 a week was given a 15% increase. A few months later a business recession necessitated a 15% decrease to all employees. What was the employee's salary after the decrease?

12. The Sweet Music Shop has a trombone priced at $175.00. This price represents a markup of 40% on cost. Find the cost.

13. A drugstore sells cosmetics at a markup of 40% on the selling price. Find the selling price for a bottle of lotion on which the markup was $1.80.

14. In problem 13, find the cost, and the cost as a per cent of the selling price.

15. A buyer purchased a job lot of 285 linen tablecloths for $1852.50. If he sold 32 of the cloths at $12.50 each, 85 at $11.50 each, 115 at $9.75 each, and the remainder at $8.25 each, find the total selling price.

16. In problem 15, find the total markup, and the markup per cent on the selling price.

17. A wholesale plumbing house prices a faucet at $15.25. If the cost was $12.85, find the markup, the markup as a per cent of selling price, and the cost as a per cent of the selling price.

18. A wholesaler sells toys at a markup of 35% on cost. Find the cost for a toy on which the markup is $1.80.

19. In problem 18, find the selling price, and the selling price as a per cent of the cost.

20. A suit was priced at $60. On a sale, the price was reduced by one-fourth. After the sale, the sale price was increased by one-fourth. What was the latest price?

21. A store, to celebrate its sixtieth anniversary, offers a 30% reduction. If a dinette was originally priced at $160, what is the reduced price? If a 3% sales tax is added to the new price, what is the total cost to a purchaser?

22. A sporting goods store sold golf balls at a markup of $2.20 per dozen. If the cost was 65% of the selling price, find the selling price per dozen.

23. A store paid $24 for table radios. If the markup was 28 per cent of the selling price, find the selling price.

24. A buyer for a store put a markup of 40% of the selling price on some women's coats that he sold at $52.50. Find the cost of the coats.

25. A firm allows discounts of $12\frac{1}{2}\%$ and 5%, and an additional discount of 1% if the bill is paid within 10 days. Find the net cost of a bill of $6842 if paid within 10 days.

26. In computing discounts an inexperienced clerk allowed a discount of 30% when he should have allowed discounts of 20% and 10%. What was the amount of the error on a bill of $820?

27. Will a buyer be better off to take discounts of 5% and 15%, or discounts of 15% and 5%?

28. The Globe Department Store uses $80,000 capital. It has $12,500 expenses and is expected to show a profit of 8% of the capital and expenses. What amount of profit is expected?

29. An article is sold for $35, and $12\frac{1}{2}\%$ is lost. What should it be sold for to gain $12\frac{1}{2}\%$?

Solution: Let 100% = the cost price
Then $87\frac{1}{2}\%$ = selling price by the first condition
and $112\frac{1}{2}\%$ = selling price by the second condition.

It is thus seen that the two selling prices are to each other as 7 to 9 and that the second is nine-sevenths of the first.

30. A wholesaler of automobile accessories sells side-view mirrors at a selling price that was 135% of the cost. If the markup was $1.80, find the selling price.

CHAPTER SEVEN

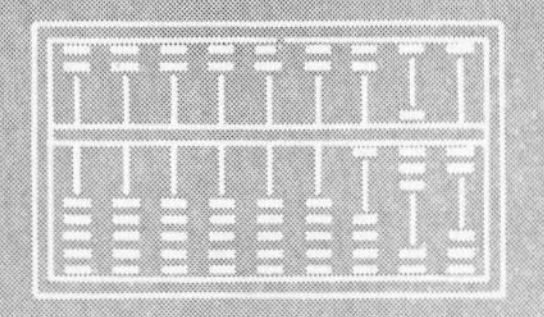

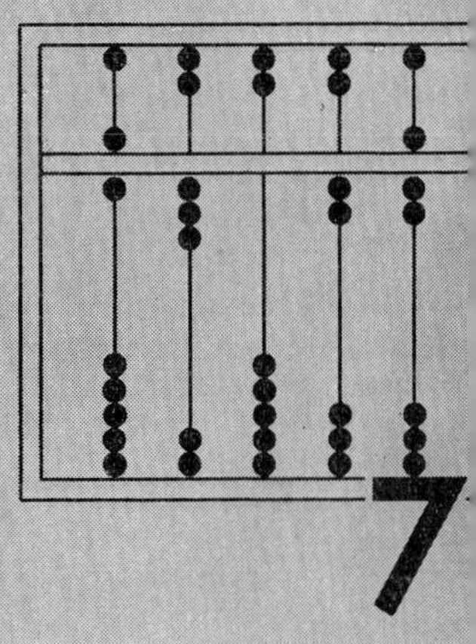

APPROXIMATE NUMBERS

1. MEASUREMENTS AND APPROXIMATE NUMBERS

People frequently have the impression that all numbers are exact and that computations involving such numbers, if performed without error, result in exact numbers. Such a situation is not always true, of course.

Exact numbers and approximate numbers form an interesting topic for discussion.

Counting is done frequently by all of us in our daily living. *When units which cannot be divided are counted and described as a certain number, that number is exact.* This means it is 100 per cent perfect. If the attendance at a basketball game is reported as 4362 on a certain night, it means exactly 4362 people. If a merchant counts and finds that he has 42 dresses and 25 hats, he means just that. If you look and find that you have $32 in your billfold, you mean exactly that amount. Calculations with exact numbers, when correctly performed, produce exact results. If 40,000 people buy football tickets at $5.00 each, the amount is $200,000.00. This $200,000.00 is the result of counting an indivisible unit, the dollar, and is an exact number.*

Numbers resulting from counting indivisible units are con-

* We speak of the dollar as being indivisible because the silver dollar and the dollar bill, as such, cannot be subdivided.

sidered to be exact. Numbers representing measurement are considered approximate numbers. We should not think of an approximate number as one that has been carelessly obtained. An approximate number is a number that does not express absolute precision, but it records to a certain degree of accuracy. We should not look upon computation with approximate numbers as computation which has not been carried out carefully. There never has been such a thing as an exact measurement of weight, time, length, area, volume, temperature and so forth. Many attempts have been made to obtain absolute standards of measurements but no perfect measurements have ever been made.

All numbers which represent measurements, as well as many other numbers, are approximate numbers. Pi, the number of times the diameter of a circle is contained in its circumference, is an approximate number. The fraction $^{22}/_7$ is a rather commonly used approximation for π, and π or pi expressed to five digits is 3.1416, an approximate number. Practically all the numbers taken from handbook tables are approximate. There are many such tables, some of which contain thousands of approximate numbers.

In discussing approximate numbers, the terms "units of measurement," and "significant digits" need to be understood.

2. UNITS OF MEASUREMENT

The unit of measurement is the smallest unit used in carrying out a measurement. If a quart jar were used to measure the water placed in a wash tub, the unit of measurement would be the quart jar. If the hand were used to measure the height of a horse, the hand would be the unit of measure. If an unmarked board one yard long were used to measure the length of a fence, the yard would be the unit of measurement. In working with approximate numbers we shall want to look for the unit of measurement which is used. In case the unit of measurement used is not obvious, it is best to use the least precise unit suggested by the given data.

In describing the distance from the earth to the sun as 93,000,000 miles it is not clear whether the distance has been measured to the nearest mile, the nearest thousand miles, or the nearest million miles. The least precise unit of measurement in this distance is 1,000,000 miles. Consequently this is the unit we shall use.

Consider the width of a desk given as 3.6 feet. Here the unit of measure is readily seen to be one tenth of a foot. The unit of measurement of 0.1 foot means that the edge of the desk has a length of 3.6 ± 0.05 feet. The measurement is recorded as 3.6 feet, but the real measurement lies anywhere between 3.55 and 3.65 feet. If the measurement of the width of the desk is listed as 3.64 feet, then 0.01 foot is immediately suggested as being the unit of measurement. The width of the desk is 3.64 ± 0.005 feet, and the true measurement is between 3.635 and 3.645 feet.

Another example is a tank said to contain 6743 gallons. Here the gallon is evidently the unit of measure. The tank would contain 6743 ± 0.5 gallons and the true measure is between 6742.5 and 6743.5 gallons.

If a vial contains 3.5679 ounces, the unit of measurement is 0.0001 ounces. The content should be expressed as 3.5679 ± 0.00005 ounces. Here the measurement is anywhere between 3.56785 and 3.56795 ounces.

If the length of a book is called $8\frac{1}{8}$ inches, the unit of measurement is $\frac{1}{8}$ inch, and the true measurement is between $8\frac{1}{16}$ inches and $8\frac{3}{16}$ inches.

3. SIGNIFICANT FIGURES

It is important to understand what is meant by the expression "significant digits," since the counting of these digits gives us one of the best ways of describing the accuracy of approximate numbers. In approximate numbers, if all the digits except the last one in a number are correct, and if the error in the last digit is not greater than one-half the unit of measurement used, then all of the digits in the approximate number are significant. Zeros may or may not be significant. Thus in a distance of 25 feet, with a unit of measurement of 1 foot, the 2 and the 5 are said to be significant. In a distance of 250 feet, with a unit of measurement of 1 foot, the 2, 5, and 0 are counters and consequently are significant. If the distance 250 feet is recorded and the unit of measurement is 10 feet, then the 25 means that there are 25 of the given units in the total distance of 250 feet. The 0 to the right of the 25 is not significant but it needs to be present as a place marker.

If a storage tank is said to contain 3600 gallons and the unit of measure is understood to be 1 gallon, the 3, 6, and the two zeros are counters and consequently every figure in the 3600 is significant. Again taking the figure 3600 gallons, but this time using the unit of measure as 100 gallons, we see that there are 36 of the 100 gallon units in the 3600 gallons. The 3 and 6 are significant but the zeros are not. However, they need to be present as place holders.

The following are the cases where zeros are significant:

(1) They are significant when they fall between digits that are significant. Thus in 603.04 feet, the unit of measurement is 0.01 foot, there is a total of 60,304 units and all 5 of the digits 6, 0, 3, 0, and 4 are significant. Also in 3004.2 pounds, the unit of measurement is 0.1 of a pound. There is a total of 30,042 units and all 5 of the digits 3, 0, 0, 4, and 2 are significant.

(2) Zeros are significant when they stand at the right of a significant digit in a decimal fraction. For example, in 0.0070 inches the unit of measure which is implied is 0.0001 inch. Here there is a total of 70 units, and the significant digits are the last two on the extreme right, namely the 7 and the 0.

(3) Zeros are significant when they stand after the decimal point in a mixed number. Consider the measurement 125.0 gallons. The unit of measurement here is apparently 0.1 of a gallon, the total number of units is 1250, and the significant digits are 1, 2, 5, and 0. In the number 603.04 referred to in a preceding paragraph, we have another example of a zero coming after the decimal point in a mixed number. Here as we have pointed out earlier we have 5 significant digits.

(4) Zeros are significant when they serve as counters of the unit of measurement used. We have in 400.34 pounds the implied unit of measurement 0.01 of a pound. Here the total number of units is 40,034, and the significant digits are 4, 0, 0, 3, and 4.

There is one instance in which zeros are not significant. They are not significant when they serve as place holders only. For instance in 0.0070 inch, where the unit of measure is implied to be 0.0001 inch, there is a total of 70 units, and the significant digits are the last two on the extreme right, namely the 7 and the zero. The other three zeros, reading from left to right, locate the decimal point.

Zeros may or may not be significant when they stand to the right of significant digits but are on the left side of the decimal point. In 5640 gallons, if the unit of measurement is 10 gallons, the zero is not significant. However, if the unit of measurement is 1 gallon, the zero is significant. Numbers used in problems may have ambiguous zeros. From this point on, in this text, we shall state the unit of measure or the number of significant digits wherever ambiguity may occur.

4. ROUNDING NUMBERS

Frequently we have a tendency to retain more digits in numbers used in computations and in the results than are justified by the original data. The main reason for this practice of using unnecessary digits is that those working with the numbers do not know how many digits should be retained. They feel obliged to use all the digits given in the numbers, and they give the final result with much greater accuracy than the original measurements justify. This type of calculating is a waste of both time and energy.

For example, in finding the circumference of a circle with a radius 8.9 feet, we should not use 3.141592653 as the value for pi, even though we know that these are the first ten digits in pi. In discussing the multiplication of approximate numbers in a later portion of this chapter we shall see that the given radius of 8.9 feet justifies using only 3.14 for pi in the computing of the circumference of the circle in question.

We have already considered to some extent in an earlier chapter the "rounding of numbers." Let us now examine this topic further. Rounding a number is the process of dropping digits from the right end of a number. We replace with zeros the digits that are dropped only when it is necessary in order to keep the decimal point in its proper place. Rounding a number is done by one of the following rules:

(1) If the digit to be dropped is less than 5, the digit on its immediate left which is to be kept should not be changed. Thus 85.642 which has five digits, when rounded to four digits, becomes 85.64.

(2) If the digit to be dropped is larger than 5, the digit on its immediate left which is to be kept should be increased by 1. Now 85.647, which has five digits, when rounded to four digits becomes 85.65.

(3) If the digit to be dropped is 5 and the digit to its immediate left is even, this digit on the immediate left, which is to be kept, is left unchanged. Thus 23.45, which has four digits, when rounded to three digits becomes 23.4.

(4) If the digit to be dropped is 5 and the digit to its immediate left is odd, this digit on the immediate left, which is to be kept, should be increased by 1. Now 23.75, which has four digits, when rounded to three digits becomes 23.8.

(5) If several digits are to be dropped from a number and the left-hand digit of those to be dropped is less than 5, the digit on its left (which is to be kept) should not be changed. If the left-hand digit of those to be dropped is 5 or larger, the digit on its immediate left (which is to be kept) should be increased by 1.

Thus 753.84739, which has eight digits, when rounded to four digits becomes 753.8. Also 234.68842, which has eight digits, when rounded to five digits becomes 234.69.

EXERCISE 1

In problems 1 through 20, give the unit of measure which is implied.

1. 635 pounds
2. 824 pounds
3. 2560 quarts
4. 8720 quarts
5. 3600 feet
6. 7200 feet
7. 35.682 feet
8. 124.395 feet
9. 45.8 miles
10. 225.7 miles
11. $45,628
12. 40,000 miles
13. $134,562
14. 120,000 miles
15. 437.05 inches
16. 7659.04 feet
17. 5.006 gallons
18. 48.0007 inches
19. $24\frac{3}{4}$ feet
20. $640\frac{5}{8}$ miles

In problems 21 through 40, give the number of significant digits in each case.

21. 7654
22. 8943
23. 67,400
24. 54,706
25. 128,605
26. 23.007
27. 38.0083
28. 60.034
29. 0.1
30. 0.01
31. 0.004
32. 0.0057
33. 5,605,702
34. 82,506,003
35. 0.0704
36. 0.08006
37. 90,608.02
38. 40,000.005
39. 60.0703
40. 0.0000503

Round the following to four significant figures.

41. 5432.8
42. 8256.4
43. 392.63
44. 437.87
45. 65.035
46. 82.645

Round the following to five significant figures.

47. 3595.55
48. 70,368.4
49. 25,136.5
50. 80,007.5
51. 91.5436
52. 8.64555

Round each of the following to tenths.

53. 64.78
54. 123.34
55. 784.857
56. 1235.764
57. 6848.96
58. 24,583.74

Round each of the following to hundredths.

59. 127.868
60. 7643.453
61. 8579.009
62. 6407.034
63. 785,884.068
64. 1,473,673.4782

5. ADDITION AND SUBTRACTION OF APPROXIMATE NUMBERS

Results obtained by computing with approximate numbers are, of course, approximate. The accuracy of this resulting approximate number depends on the accuracy of each number appearing in the calculations. Let us set up rules for handling the results of these calculations. These rules should serve two purposes:

(1) It is desirable to keep in the final result only those digits which are correct or likely to be correct. In other words, the results should be written so as to be consistent with the practices already described in connection with approximate numbers.

(2) It is well to eliminate all calculations which do not affect the final result. As we have pointed out earlier in this chapter, it is a complete waste of time in computing the area and circumference of a circle with radius 3.6 inches, to use an approximation for pi to ten decimal places.

Let us use the following practices in adding and subtracting approximate numbers:

(1) Round each number so as to carry not more than one

smaller place value (one more decimal place) than the term having the least precision.

(2) Round the sum or difference of the terms in a set to the same number of places as the term having the least precision.

For example, add: 437.563 + 98.4 + 36.5432 + 16.58 + 0.0567.

These become:
```
437.56
 98.4
 36.54
 16.58
  0.06
------
589.14 or 589.1
```

The term having the least precision is 98.4. It is precise to tenths. Thus, each of the other addends is rounded to hundredths, eliminating unnecessary computation. The sum of the rounded numbers is obtained according to the usual method of addition and then rounded to tenths in order to agree with the 98.4.

As another example, subtract 85.78 from 683.2187.

```
683.219
 85.78
-------
597.439 or 597.44
```

EXERCISE 2

Add the following approximate numbers.

1. 2137.67 + 83.972 + 143.47 + 97483.8967 + 603.28963
2. 8147.673 + 759.4 + 24.66 + 314.587 + 0.0463 + 27.506

3.
```
 614.38
  59.4786
   0.614
   7.5328
9562.9999
  38.76435
```

4.
```
10537.6
  429.583
    0.07
 7654.6794
   29.0
  879.463
```

5. Write in words each of the addends in problem 3 and also the sum.

6. Write in words each of the addends in problem 4 and also the sum.

7. 439.679
   − 26.54

8. 657.2793
   − 49.38

9. 5846.5073
   − 723.412

10. 87691.27
   − 436.8

11. 97843.28
   − 61.0

12. 529.934
   − 16.07

13. Mr. Roark travels the following distances each day during a week. Find his total mileage for the week: 128.3 miles, 75.8 miles, 62.4 miles, 246.7 miles, and 16.9 miles. His average week's driving is 650 miles. By how much is his driving for this week below his average week?

14. The Circle O Dairy weighs in the following amounts of milk in a week. Find the total for the week: 2486.4 pounds, 2470.8 pounds, 2503.6 pounds, 2491.9 pounds, 2364.7 pounds, 2511.9 pounds, and 2421.6 pounds.

15. The sides of a field are found by measurement to be 684.3 feet, 532.65 feet, 1025.4 feet, and 472.758 feet. Find the distance around the field.

16. The monthly rainfall in East Texas measured as follows: 5.64 inches, 4.7 inches, 2.03 inches, 4.6 inches, 5.31 inches, 3.4 inches, 4.61 inches, 1.2 inches, 2.61 inches, 3.38 inches, 3.4 inches, and 2.65 inches. Find the total rainfall for the year. If the average yearly rainfall is 47.6 inches, how does the year in question compare with the average?

17. The following amounts of gasoline are purchased on a trip: 14.7 gallons, 12 gallons, 13.5 gallons, 11.7 gallons, 13.3 gallons, and 12.8 gallons. Find the total amount of gasoline bought.

18. The sides of a triangular field are measured as follows: 942.68 feet, 357.7 feet, and 829.559 feet. Find the distance around the field.

19. The hours of daylight in a week are measured for each day as follows: 12.6 hours, 12.58 hours, 12.5 hours, 12.47 hours, 12.43 hours, 12.38 hours, and 12.32 hours. Find the total number of daylight hours in the week.

20. In Miss Barton's typewriting class 5 speed tests are given in a week. The lengths of these tests are as follows: 48.7 minutes,

37.5 minutes, 26.8 minutes, 25 minutes, and 16.4 minutes. What is the total time devoted to speed tests in a week?

6. MULTIPLICATION AND DIVISION OF APPROXIMATE NUMBERS

Consider a rectangular strip of land 15.5 feet long and 25.5 feet wide. If we declare the area to be 395.25 square feet we are not being very realistic. The unit of measurement used for the sides does not justify the degree of refinement in measure which we have used to express the area. The long side of the rectangle could have varied from 25.45 feet to 25.55 feet. The short side could have varied from 15.45 feet to 15.55 feet. If the measurements had been 25.45 feet and 15.45 feet, which are the minimum possible lengths, the minimum area would be 393.20 square feet. If the measurements had been 15.55 feet and 25.55 feet, the maximum possible lengths, the maximum area would have been 397.30 square feet. We know that the true area of the rectangle falls somewhere between 393.20 square feet and 397.30 square feet. Let us notice that there are 4.1 square feet between the possible limits, and there is no justification in giving the computed area of 395.25 square feet any more accurately than the nearest square foot. This decision leads us to accept 395 square feet as the most probable area. It contains the same number of significant digits as the original linear measurements.

We shall follow two rules in the multiplication of approximate numbers.

(1) In finding the product of two approximate numbers, each of which has the same number of significant digits, keep the same number of significant digits in the product as are in the multiplier or the multiplicand.

(2) In finding the product of two approximate numbers, one of which contains more significant digits than the other, round the more accurate of the numbers to be multiplied until it contains one more significant digit than the other before multiplying. The product should be rounded until it contains the same number of significant digits as appear in the less accurate of the numbers to be multiplied.

As we have already noted, an exact number differs from an approximate number in that an exact number represents a true count. We shall follow this rule in multiplying an exact number by an approximate number.

(3) In finding the product of an exact number and an approximate number, keep in the product the same number of significant digits as appear in the given approximate number.

As an example of rule 1, multiply 16.57 by 43.12.

```
   16.57
   43.12
--------
    3314
   1657
  4971
 6628
--------
714.4984
```

This product rounds to 714.5.

As an example of rule 2, multiply 58.7921 by 16.3. Before multiplying, round the 58.7921 to 58.79.

```
  58.79
   16.3
-------
  17637
 35274
 5879
-------
958.277
```

This product will be rounded to 958.

To illustrate rule 3, multiply 358.62 by 15. In this example, we are considering that the 15 is an exact number and the 358.62 is an approximate number.

```
 358.62
     15
-------
 179310
 35862
-------
5379.30
```

This product rounds to 5379.3.

In solving a problem based on multiplying together *more than two approximate numbers*, find the product of two of the approximate numbers, round this partial product to one more digit than will be retained in the final answer, and use this rounded product with a third approximate number to find a new product. Continue the process until all the multiplications have been completed. Round the final product so that it contains the same number of significant digits appearing in the least accurate of the approximate numbers to be multiplied. For example, take $57.32 \times 14.6 \times 892.47$.

```
   57.32
 × 14.6
 -------
   34392
  22928
  5732
 -------
 836.872
```

We shall round this to 836.9. Now multiply 836.9 by 892.5, which is 892.47 rounded to four significant digits.

```
      892.5
    × 836.9
 ----------
      80325
     53550
    26775
   71400
 ----------
 746,933.25
```

This number will round to 747,000, the zeros being insignificant.

Division of approximate numbers is carried on according to the following rules:

(1) In finding the quotient of two approximate numbers, each of which has the same number of significant digits, divide the given dividend by the divisor until the quotient has one more significant digit than the divisor or dividend. The quotient is then rounded to the same number of significant digits as the divisor or dividend.

Consider 68.3 divided by 25.4.

```
               2.688   This result rounds to 2.69.
     25.4 / 68.3.00
              50 8
              ------
              17 50
              15 24
              ------
               2 260
               2 032
              ------
                2280
                2032
              ------
```

(2) In finding the quotient of two approximate numbers, one of which has more significant digits than the other, round the more accurate number until it has one more significant digit than the less accurate number. Divide the given dividend by the divisor until the quotient has one more significant digit than the less accurate number appearing in the dividend or the divisor. Then round the quotient so that it has the same number of significant digits as the less accurate number appearing in the dividend or in the divisor. Consider 65.238 divided by 4.7. Here the dividend, 65.238, is rounded to 65.2, in accordance with the foregoing rule.

```
Now:            13.8
        4.7 / 65.2.0
              47
              -----
              18 2
              14 1
              -----
               4 10
               3 76
              -----
```

The 13.8 is rounded to 14, which is the final answer according to the rule just described.

(3) In finding the quotient of an approximate and an exact

number, divide the given dividend by the divisor until the quotient has one more significant digit than the given approximate number contains. Round the quotient so that it contains the same number of significant digits as the given approximate number contains.

As an illustration, consider the approximate number 5.873 divided by the exact number 15.

```
       0.39153
15 / 5.8730
     4 5
     ----
     1 37
     1 35
     ----
        23
        15
        --
         80
         75
         --
          50
          45
          --
```

This quotient rounds to 0.3915.

EXERCISE 3

Multiply the following, assuming all numbers are approximate unless otherwise indicated.

1. $67.3 \times 84.7 =$
2. $104.3 \times 625.9 =$
3. $792.43 \times 57.5 =$
4. $8603.4 \times 425.6 =$
5. $99{,}857.34 \times 867.62 =$
6. $252{,}898.63 \times 2347.87 =$
7. $21 \times 68.42 =$ (Assume the 21 is an exact number.)
8. $972.38 \times 16 =$ (Assume the 16 is an exact number.)
9. $625 \times 47 =$ (Assume both numbers are exact.)

10. 835 × 53 = (Assume both numbers are exact.)

11. 5643.67 × 7439.82 =

12. 3795.79 × 7384.67 =

13. Read the numbers which are to be multiplied together in problem 11. Read the number which represents the product after this number has been rounded consistently according to significant digits.

14. Read the numbers which are to be multiplied together in problem 12. Read the number which represents the product after this number has been rounded consistently according to significant digits.

15. 83.67 × 157.93 × 29.6 =

16. 269.78 × 983.67 × 37.8 =

17. 5864.63 × 461.82 × 79.632 =

18. 2984.39 × 162.7 × 38.7 × 793.8 =

19. 78,653.921 × 12,487.782 × 653.2 × 81.5 =

20. 53.9 × 728.63 × 98.72 × 3.7 × 15.7 =

Divide the following, assuming all numbers are approximate unless otherwise indicated.

21. 15.2 ÷ 6.23 =

22. 224.7 ÷ 5.321 =

23. 8738.9 ÷ 14.62 =

24. 16.72 ÷ 43.957 =

25. 2839.62 ÷ 278.59 =

26. 2746.5 ÷ 74,392.42 =

27. 657.3 ÷ 72 = (Assume 72 is an exact number.)

28. 684 ÷ 25.73 = (Assume 684 is an exact number.)

29. $27 \overline{)439.26}$ (Assume 27 is an exact number.)

30. $463 \overline{)1684.273}$ (Assume 463 is an exact number.)

31. $4753 \overline{)2{,}989{,}637}$ (Assume the dividend and divisor are both exact here.)

32. $12{,}823 \overline{)6{,}885{,}951}$ (Assume the dividend and divisor are both exact here.)

33. Read in words the divisor and dividend in problem 31. Also read the quotient.

34. Read in words the divisor and dividend in problem 32. Also read the quotient.

35. 15.678 / 247.63

36. 62.432 / 4692.831

37. 16.5793 / 203.7921

38. 439.6847 / 2307.6432

39. Read in words the divisor and dividend in problem 37. Also read the quotient.

40. Read in words the divisor and dividend in problem 38. Also read the quotient.

41. The lengths of the sides of a rectangle are measured with the use of a ruler graduated in tenths of an inch. The length of one side is read as 36.5 inches. The length of the other side is read as 42.3 inches. What is the smallest value which the area of this rectangle can have? What is the largest value which the area of the rectangle can have? Using the rules governing approximate numbers, give the area of this rectangle.

42. An acre contains 43,560 square feet. A piece of land is measured and the length is given as 482 feet and the width as 739 feet. How many acres does the plot contain, if we assume that the 482 and the 739 are approximate numbers and the 43,560 is exact?

43. How many square feet are in the piece of land described in problem 42?

44. A rectangular piece of carpet material is measured with a tape measure marked in units of ⅛ foot. The carpet is said to be 15 feet wide and 24 feet long. What is the minimum area of carpet here?

45. What is the maximum area of carpet in problem 44?

46. Find the circumference of a circle of radius 6.8 inches, given $\pi = 3.1415926$.

47. Find the area of the circle described in problem 46.

48. Ranches are frequently measured in sections. A section contains 640 acres. How many acres are in a ranch which is said to contain 82.7 sections? Assume the 640 is an exact number.

49. The specific gravity of a substance is equal to the weight of a given volume of the substance divided by the weight of an

equal volume of water. If we assume that water weighs 62.4 pounds per cubic foot and aviation gasoline weighs 45 pounds per cubic foot, what is the specific gravity of aviation gasoline?

50. The diagonal of a square is equal to the length of the side multiplied by 1.4142136. What is the diagonal of a square whose sides are 17.53 inches?

51. There is approximately 0.4535924277 kilogram in a pound. A boy weighs 183 pounds. How many kilograms does he weigh?

52. How many pounds of milk testing 4.4% butterfat are needed to give 83 pounds of butterfat?

53. The live weight of a calf was 270 pounds. The dressed weight was 165 pounds. What was the per cent loss in weight?

54. On a test Robert had 12 problems correct out of 15. What per cent of the problems did he have correct?

55. A boat has a triangular sail with a base of 6 yards and a height of 8.5 yards. Find the area of the sail in square yards.

56. The Blackjack School playground has an area of 3562 square yards. If the width is 63 yards, find the length in yards.

57. Multiply 632.58 feet by 0.3459 and add 231.4 feet.

58. A turkey weighs 5.8 pounds. What will it cost at 58.3 cents a pound?

59. How far is it around a piece of land represented by a rectangle 16 inches by 21 inches on a map to the scale of 1 inch = 0.8 mile?

60. The IJ Warehouse sold 65 barrels of apples at $12.60 a barrel, and charged 18 cents a barrel for storage and a commission of 5½%. Find the net proceeds of the sale.

CHAPTER EIGHT

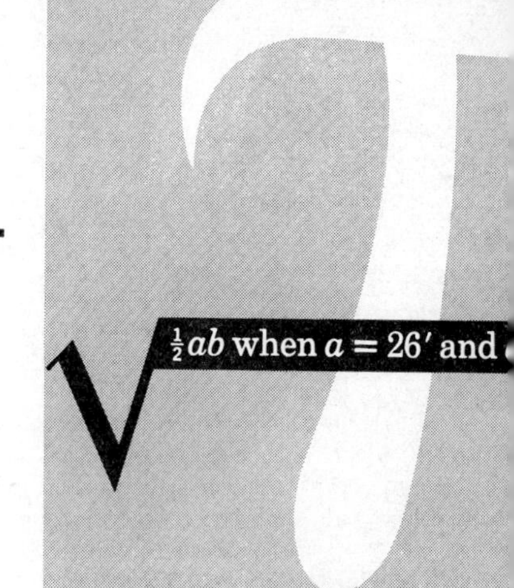

$A = \frac{1}{2}ab$
$A = \frac{1}{2} \times 26 \times$
$A = 260$ sq. ft

$A = \pi\ dh + \frac{1}{2}\ \pi$

ELEMENTARY ALGEBRA

1. INTRODUCTION

Algebra is quite similar to arithmetic. It requires our careful concentration and persistent effort if we are to succeed with it. We have already observed that these traits are highly desirable as we have worked through the first seven chapters of this book.

Algebra may be said to be an extension of arithmetic in that, in algebra, letters are used to represent numbers. Thus algebra generalizes arithmetic. For example, dog food sells for 20 cents per can. Two cans will cost 40 cents, 3 cans will cost 60 cents and N cans will cost 20 times N cents or 20 N cents, or $0.20N$ dollars. This gives us a formula that will work regardless of the number of cans of dog food purchased. Also if N represents the number of cans of dog food we buy one week, and we buy three times as many cans the following week, then we buy 3 times N or $3N$ cans of dog food the following week.

Algebra utilizes the principles we have learned in arithmetic. Thus the four fundamental processes, indicated by the symbols $+$, $-$, $\times$, $\div$ have the same meaning when applied to algebra that they had in arithmetic.

Any combination of numbers and letters or of letters, and the four fundamental processes is called an algebraic expression. Parts of these expressions which are separated from each other by the signs + or − are known as terms. Thus $4a + 3b - 6m$ is an algebraic expression consisting of three terms. When no sign is written in front of a term, the sign + is understood. The $4a$ in the above expression is understood to be plus.

If an algebraic expression contains one term it is called a simple expression. If it has two or more terms it is a multiple expression.

There are other common ways to describe algebraic expressions. Those with one term are called monomials. For example, $5a$ is a monomial. An expression with two terms, such as $2c + 3m$, is called a binomial, and an expression with three terms, such as $4x + 7y - 9z$, is called a trinomial. The name multinomial refers to all multiple expressions, such as binomials and trinomials.

When two or more quantities are multiplied together the result is known as the product of the quantities. When we use letters to represent numbers, there can be misunderstanding between the multiplication sign and the letters x and X. Consequently, we indicate multiplication in algebra either (1) by using a period halfway up between the letters, (2) by writing the letters in succession with no symbol between them, or (3) by writing each factor in parentheses. Now the product of c and d may be written either as $c \cdot d$, or cd, or $(c)(d)$.

Each of the quantities multiplied together to form a product is known as a factor of the product. Thus, 2, x, and y are the factors of the product $2xy$. Two is called the numerical factor, and x and y are literal factors.

The numerical factor in an algebraic expression is called the coefficient of the remaining factors. In the expression $2xy$, 2 is the coefficient, and xy is the literal coefficient of 2. The quantity x has the same meaning as $1x$. If the coefficient of a letter is not explicitly written, it is understood to be 1.

A power of a quantity is the result obtained when multiplying the quantity by itself any number of times. This multiplication is indicated by writing to the right and above the quantity a number which indicates the number of factors to be taken.

Thus:

$b \times b$ is called the second power of b, and is written b^2;
$b \times b \times b$ is the third power of b, and is written b^3; and
$b \times b \times b \times b$ is the fourth power of b, and is written b^4.

The small number which indicates the power of any quantity is known as an exponent. Thus 2, 3, and 4 are the exponents of a^2, a^3, and a^4 respectively:

a^2 is generally read "a square";
a^3 is generally read "a cube"; and
a^4 is generally read "a to the fourth."

For example, $3a^4 + 2a^2 + 5a$ is read "three a to the fourth plus two a square plus five a."

The quantity x has the same meaning as x^1. If the power of a quantity is not explicitly written, it is understood to be 1.

For example, find the difference in meaning between $3x$ and x^3. By $3x$ we mean the result of multiplying 3 by x. By x^3, we mean the product of x and x and x. If $x = 2$, then $3x = 3 \cdot x = 3 \cdot 2 = 6$, but $x^3 = x \cdot x \cdot x = 2 \cdot 2 \cdot 2 = 8$.

Now, find the value of $6c^4$ when $c = 4$. But $6c^4 = 6 \cdot c \cdot c \cdot c \cdot c = 6 \cdot 4 \cdot 4 \cdot 4 \cdot 4 = 1536$.

As another example, find the value of $ab + bc - ac$ when $a = 3$, $b = 2$, and $c = 5$. Now $ab = 3 \cdot 2 = 6$; $bc = 2 \cdot 5 = 10$; and $ac = 3 \cdot 5 = 15$. Then $ab + bc - ac = 6 - 10 - 15 = 1$.

Also find $3(x + y)(x - y)$ where $x = 5$ and $y = 2$. The parentheses denote multiplication. Then $3(x + y)(x - y) = 3(5 + 2)(5 - 2) = 3(7)(3) = 63$.

EXERCISE 1

Write each of the following in words. Then give the coefficient and the exponent of each letter.

1. $4x^2$ 2. $6x^3$ 3. $15x^3z^4$
4. $12a^2b^3$ 5. $35a^4b^5c^6$ 6. $12m^{15}$
7. $\frac{3}{4}x^2y^3$ 8. $\frac{2}{3}m^2n^3$ 9. $14x^3y^2z^4$ 10. $49x^7y^8$

Write each of the following in exponent form.

11. $4xxy$ 12. $15aab$ 13. $aaaaa$
14. $aaabb$ 15. $42xxxyy$ 16. $\frac{3}{4}lllnnn$
17. $184xxxx^3yyy$ 18. $24xxyyyzz$ 19. $42ccccc^2dd$
20. $36aaaa^4bb$

Find the value of the following when $a = 1$, $b = 2$, $c = 3$, and $d = 4$.

21. a^2b^2 22. a^3c^3 23. $6a^2 + b$

24. $9abc$ 25. $7b + 2c - 3d$ 26. $\frac{b + c}{5}$

27. $\frac{2b + 3d}{4}$ 28. $\frac{d - a}{2}$ 29. $ab + bc + 3cd$

30. $(3a + b - c)^5$ 31. $\frac{b + c}{a} - \frac{2d - b}{c}$

32. $4b + 2(a + 3c - d)$ 33. $(bc)^3 - (cd)^2$

34. $b^5 - \frac{1}{4} cd^2$ 35. $8d - 3(a + 2b + c)$

36. $5(a + b)(d - b)$ 37. $9(abcd)$

38. $\frac{25a^2b^3}{5c^2d^3}$ 39. $\frac{c + 2d - b}{a + 2b - c}$ 40. d^5

2. NEGATIVE NUMBERS

Negative numbers appear frequently in algebra. In order to illustrate the basic relation between positive and negative numbers, let us consider the positive numbers as so many points along a line, each a measured distance to the right of a reference

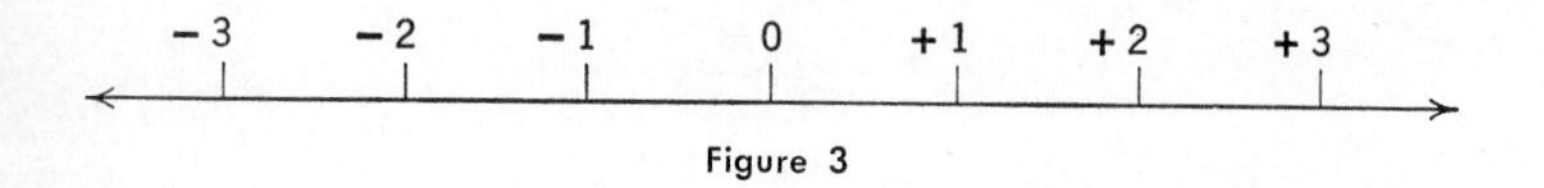

Figure 3

point called zero (0). We shall extend the line to the left of the zero point. We can measure off on the line to the left the same distances from zero that we have measured to the right. Numbers to identify these points on the left are known as *negative numbers*. These numbers are written with a minus sign (−) in front of them, in contrast with positive numbers, which are preceded by a plus sign (+). A number written without a sign is considered a positive number.

When we are thinking only in terms of measured distances, regardless of direction, we use *absolute values*. The absolute value of a number disregards the sign attached to the number. We designate absolute value of a number m by enclosing it between two parallel bars $|m|$. Thus $|-5| = |+5| = 5$.

The following are *rules* for *adding and subtracting signed numbers.*

1. When the addends have like signs:
   (*a*) Add the absolute values of the addends.
   (*b*) Place the common sign before the sum in step *a*.
2. When the addends have unlike signs:
   (*a*) Subtract the smaller of the two absolute values from the larger.
   (*b*) Place the sign of the addend with the larger absolute value in front of the difference of step *a*.

For example:

1. Where the signs are alike:
   (*a*) $(+3) + (+9) = +|3 + 9| = +12$ or 12
   (*b*) $(-4) + (-7) = -|4 + 7| = -11$
2. Where the signs are unlike:
   (*a*) $(-7) + (+4) = -|7 - 4| = -3$
   (*b*) $(+16) + (-10) = +|16 - 10| = +6$ or 6

To subtract two signed numbers:

(*a*) Change the sign of the subtrahend (this is the number to to be subtracted).

(*b*) Add the changed subtrahend and the minuend by following the rule previously given for the addition of two signed numbers.

For example:

1. Subtract: $(+9) - (+3)$
   (*a*) $(+3)$ changes to (-3)
   (*b*) $(+9) + (-3) = +6$ or 6
2. Subtract: $(+7) - (-3)$
   (*a*) (-3) changes to $(+3)$
   (*b*) $(+7) + (+3) = +10$ or 10
3. Subtract: $(-15) - (+8)$
   (*a*) $(+8)$ changes to (-8)
   (*b*) $(-15) + (-8) = -23$

The following *rule* applies to *multiplying signed numbers.*

1. When the signs of two numbers are alike:
   (*a*) Obtain the product of the absolute values of the numbers.
   (*b*) Place a plus sign before the product in step *a*.
2. When the signs of the two numbers are not alike:
   (*a*) Obtain the product of the absolute values of the numbers.
   (*b*) Place a minus sign before the product in step *a*.

For example,

1. Where the signs are alike:
   (*a*) $(+6) \times (+4) = +|6 \times 4| = +24$ or 24
   (*b*) $(-8) \times (-5) = +|8 \times 5| = +40$ or 40
2. Where the signs are unlike:
   (*a*) $(+7) \times (-9) = -|7 \times 9| = -63$
   (*b*) $(-8) \times (+4) = -|8 \times 4| = -32$

The following *rule* applies to *dividing signed numbers.*

1. When the signs of the divisor and dividend are alike:
   (*a*) Divide the absolute value of the divisor into the absolute value of the dividend.
   (*b*) Place a plus sign before the quotient obtained in the step above.
2. When the signs of the divisor and dividend are not alike:
   (*a*) Divide the absolute value of the divisor into the absolute value of the dividend.
   (*b*) Place a minus sign before the quotient obtained in the step above.

For example:

1. Where the signs are alike:
   (*a*) $(+8) \div (+2) = +|8 \div 2| = +4$ or 4
   (*b*) $(-18) \div (-6) = +|18 \div 6| = +3$ or 3
2. Where the signs are unlike:
   (*a*) $(-18) \div (+6) = -|18 \div 6| = -3$
   (*b*) $(+24) \div (-3) = -|24 \div 3| = -8$

EXERCISE 2

Add the following:

1. $(-15) + (-10)$
2. $(-18) + (-14)$
3. $(+23) + (-5)$
4. $(+64) + (-22)$
5. $(-34) + (+16)$
6. $(-124) + (+42)$
7. $(+246\frac{3}{4}) + (-38\frac{1}{2})$
8. $(+439\frac{1}{16}) + (-216\frac{3}{8})$
9. $(-384\frac{3}{16}) + (+142\frac{1}{5})$
10. $(-265\frac{3}{4}) + (+32\frac{3}{32})$

Subtract the following:

11. $(+16) - (+5)$
12. $(+25) - (-8)$
13. $(-34) - (-16)$
14. $(-52) - (-13)$

15. $(-65) - (-32)$
16. $(+133) - (+62\frac{3}{4})$
17. $(-28\frac{5}{6}) - (-103\frac{3}{4})$
18. $(-45.7) - (+16.03)$
19. $(-126.9) - (+205.8)$
20. $(+79.4) - (-164.3)$

Multiply the following:

21. $(+6)(+5)$
22. $(+15)(+7)$
23. $(-4)(-9)$
24. $(-14)(-6)$
25. $(+23)(-4)$
26. $(-16)(+12)$
27. $(-2.28)(+15.3)$
28. $(-57\frac{1}{2})(+13\frac{3}{4})$
29. $(-126\frac{1}{8})(-176\frac{3}{4})$
30. $(-0.238)(-16.54)$

Divide the following:

31. $(+16) \div (+4)$
32. $(-32) \div (-8)$
33. $(+81) \div (-9)$
34. $(-34) \div (+17)$
35. $(-126) \div (-21)$
36. $(+18.2) \div (-9.1)$
37. $(-6.48) \div (+32.4)$
38. $(-12\frac{1}{4}) \div (-6\frac{1}{2})$
39. $(+0.0078) \div (+0.39)$
40. $(-15.3) \div (+5.1)$

3. SOLVING SIMPLE LINEAR EQUATIONS

In our work in arithmetic we have solved many problems dealing with "unknown numbers." Consistently with the four fundamental operations, addition, subtraction, multiplication and division, these problems appeared as one of four basic types illustrated as follows:

I. What number increased by 5 equals 15?
II. What number decreased by 5 equals 15?
III. What number multiplied by 5 equals 15?
IV. What number divided by 5 equals 15?

In answering these questions, let us think of them as being in the following form:

I. $? + 5 = 15$, II. $? - 5 = 15$, III. $(?)(5) = 15$, IV. $?/5 = 15$.

In algebra we let x (or any other letter) represent the unknown quantity which we seek. An equation is a statement of equality between two quantities. Now we may write the equations referred to just above, replacing the question mark by x in each instance.

I. $x + 5 = 15$, II. $x - 5 = 15$, III. $5x = 15$, IV. $x/5 = 15$

A statement that two expressions are equal, such as we see in

I, II, III, and IV above, is called an equation. The terms on the left of the sign of equality are called the left member or left side of the equation. The terms on the right are called the right member or right side of the equation. A number which reduces both members to the same number when it is substituted for the unknown in an equation is said to be a root or solution of the equation. It also satisfies the equation.

The solutions for the four equations given above are: I. $x = 10$, II. $x = 20$, III. $x = 3$, and IV. $x = 75$

The following rule is basic in the handling of equations: *If equal numbers are increased, decreased, multiplied, or divided by the same number, the resulting numbers will be equal. We shall exclude division by zero.*

Consider the equation $15 = 15$. It makes no difference what number we either add to or subtract from both members of this equation. The resulting numbers will always be equal.

Given: $15 = 15$

$15 + 2 = 15 + 2$, adding 2 to both sides

$17 = 17$, the results are equal

Given: $15 = 15$

$15 - 2 = 15 - 2$, subtracting 2 from both sides

$13 = 13$, the results are equal

Given: $15 = 15$

$15 - 18 = 15 - 18$, subtracting 18 from both sides

$-3 = -3$, the results are equal

Given: $15 = 15$

$15 \cdot 5 = 15 \cdot 5$, multiplying both sides by 5

$75 = 75$, the results are equal

Given: $15 = 15$

$\frac{15}{5} = \frac{15}{5}$, dividing both members by 5

$3 = 3$, the results are equal

Given: $x + 5 = 15$

$x + 5 - 5 = 15 - 5$, subtracting 5 from both sides

$x = 10$, simplifying

Given: $x - 5 = 15$

$x - 5 + 5 = 15 + 5$, adding 5 to both sides

$x = 20$, simplifying

Given: $5x = 15$

$$\frac{5x}{5} = \frac{15}{5}, \text{ dividing both sides by 5}$$

$$x = 3, \text{ simplifying}$$

Given: $\frac{x}{5} = 15$

$$\frac{x}{5} \cdot 5 = 15 \cdot 5, \text{ multiplying both sides by 5}$$

$$x = 75, \text{ simplifying}$$

Once we arrive at what apparently is the solution to an equation, it is important to see if this solution satisfies the equation. This procedure is called checking the solution. A value of the unknown, which satisfies an equation, is called a *solution* of the equation.

Solve and check the equation $x + 7 = 12$.

$x = 12 - 7$, subtracting 7 from both sides
$x = 5$, simplifying

To check, we replace the x in the original equation by 5.

Then: $5 + 7 = 12$
and $12 = 12$, simplifying

Solve and check the equation $8x = 48$.

$x = \frac{48}{8}$, dividing both sides by 8

$x = 6$, simplifying

To check, we replace the x in the original equation by 6.

Then: $8 \cdot 6 = 48$
$48 = 48$, simplifying

Solve and check the equation $x - 4.7 = 5.3$ (decimals)

$x = 5.3 + 4.7$, adding 4.7 to both sides
$x = 10.0$, simplifying

To check, we replace the x in the original equation by 10.0.

Then: $10.0 - 4.7 = 5.3$
$5.3 = 5.3$, simplifying

Solve and check the equation $\frac{x}{7} = 4$.

$x = 7 \cdot 4$, multiplying both sides by 7
$x = 28$, simplifying

To check, we replace the x in the original equation by 28.

Then: $\frac{28}{7} = 4$

$4 = 4$, simplifying

Solve and check $5x + 4 = -21$.

$5x = -25$, adding -4 to each side
$x = -5$, simplifying

In checking $x = -5$ as the solution of $5x = -25$, we have $(5)(-5) = -25$.

$-25 = -25$, simplifying

Solving word problems is fascinating. If we take each part of the problem, study it carefully, and then put together our various conclusions, we can be quite successful with word problems in algebra.

For example, one number is 7 more than three times the other, and their sum is 35. Find the numbers.

We shall begin by letting x equal one number. The other number will be $7 + 3x$. Adding the expressions for the two numbers we have $x + 7 + 3x$, which equals 35. Then solving $x + 7 + 3x = 35$, we have $4x = 35 - 7$ or $4x = 28$. Then $x = 7$ is one number. The other number is $7 + 3x$ or $7 + 3(7)$ or $7 + 21$ or 28.

To check we go back to the original wording of the problem. We have found that one number is 28. This is 7 more than three times 7 which is the other number. Also the sum of the numbers 7 and 28 is 35.

EXERCISE 3

Solve and check the following equations.

1. $x + 5 = 9$
2. $x - 3 = 7$
3. $x + 14 = 9$
4. $x + 7 = 5$
5. $3x = 18$
6. $4x = 24$

7. $x - 4 = 3\frac{1}{2}$

8. $x + 9 = 11\frac{3}{4}$

9. $\frac{x}{5} = 3$

10. $\frac{x}{7} = 8\frac{1}{7}$

11. $x - 3\frac{1}{2} = 4\frac{1}{4}$

12. $x + \frac{1}{3} = 2\frac{3}{4}$

13. $\frac{x}{8} = 4\frac{3}{4}$

14. $\frac{x}{4} = \frac{3}{4}$

15. $5x = 75.5$

16. $x + 3.24 = 6.18$

17. $5x - 15 = 2x$

18. $3x + 6 = x$

19. $\frac{3x}{4} + 6 = \frac{x}{2} + 8$

20. $\frac{5x}{6} - 4 = \frac{x}{3} + 10$

21. $3\frac{1}{5}x - 8 = 2x + 6$

22. $18x - 7 = 14x + 5$

23. $\frac{2x}{3} + 15 = 18$

24. $\frac{x}{2} + \frac{x}{3} = 10$

25. $\frac{3x}{5} + \frac{x}{8} = 29$

26. $2\frac{3}{5}x + 9 = 1\frac{2}{3}x - 5$

27. $6 - 5(4x - 3) = 14(2x + 4) - 52$

28. $24 + 3(2x - 5) = 16(3x - 7) + 14$

29. $41 + 2(3x + 4) = 17(2x - 5) + 15$

30. $4(6x - 7) - 3(2x + 1) = 15(3x - 2) + 4(2x - 5)$

31. One number is 7 more than another and their sum is **147**. Find the numbers.

32. 40% of what number equals 32?

33. The sum of three consecutive even integers is 144. Find the integers. (Hint: Let the first even number be n, the next will then be $n + 2$, and the third will be $n + 4$.)

34. Three times what number is 35 more than two-thirds of that number?

35. The larger of two numbers exceeds twice the smaller by 5. If the sum of the numbers is 95, what are the numbers? (Hint: Let the smaller number be x, then the larger number is $2x + 5$.)

36. Five less than seven times a certain number is the same as three more than six times the number. Find the number.

37. A man is five times as old as his daughter and his

daughter is three years younger than his son. If their combined ages total 66 years, how old is each?

38. A team played a total of 162 games and won 46 games more than it lost. How many games did it win?

39. Two partners divided $20,000; the second partner receiving three times as much as the first. How much did each receive?

40. A piece of rope 8 feet long is cut into 3 pieces, so that one piece is three times as long as the shortest piece and the longest piece is four times as long as the shortest piece. What is the length of the 3 pieces?

41. Three-fourths of a number is equal to five more than one-eighth of the number. Find the number.

42. Fifty-five dollars are to be divided among 4 boys and 3 girls, so that each of the boys receives twice as much as each of the girls. How much does each receive?

43. The sum of three consecutive integers is 84. Find the integers.

44. A girl spent two-thirds of her money for a book and one-eighth of her money for a pen. The remaining $1.75 she saved. How much money did she have in the first place?

45. Robert is 5 years older than his sister, and the sum of their ages is 73 years. How old is Robert?

4. SOME FORMULAS FROM COMMERCIAL ALGEBRA

Let us now consider some of the more basic formulas that have frequent application in the business world.

When we rent a house for the family we expect to pay for the use of the house. When we borrow money we expect to pay for the use of the money. The money we pay for the use of the house is called *rent*. The amount paid for the use of money is called *interest*.

Suppose you borrow $800 for 3 months at 8%. If you borrowed $800 for one year at 8% you would pay

$$\$800 \times 0.08 = \$64.00$$

But 3 months are one-fourth of a year. Now, $\frac{1}{4} \times \$64.00 = \$16.00$. This is the amount of interest you owe on the $800. A rather simple way to look at the problem is to take the formula $I = prt$. Here I represents the interest, p the principal, r the rate, and t *the time in years.* A *formula* is an *equation* in which the letters refer to definite quantities.

Thus, in the example to which we have just referred, $p = \$800$, $r = 8\%$ or 0.08 and $t = \frac{1}{4}$. Now in $I = prt$, $I = \left(\overset{8}{\cancel{800}}\right)\left(\frac{\overset{2}{\cancel{8}}}{\cancel{100}}\right)\left(\frac{1}{\underset{1}{\cancel{4}}}\right)$, or $I = \$16.00$.

In repaying the loan of \$800 plus interest you will pay a total of \$816. It is convenient to express this through the formula $A = P + I$, in which A represents the final amount to be paid, P is the principal, and I the interest. In the illustration of borrowing \$800 for 3 months at 8%, we have $P = \$800$, $I = \$16$ and A, the total amount to be repaid, is $A = \$800 + \$16 = \$816$.

The formula $I = prt$ becomes $t = \frac{I}{pr}$ upon solving for t.

If we wish to determine how long \$1000 is borrowed at 6% when \$20 interest is due at the time the loan is repaid, then $p = \$1000$, $r = 0.06$, and $I = \$20$.

$$t = \frac{20}{(1000)(.06)} = \frac{20}{60} = \frac{1}{3}$$

Since t represents the time in years, we have one-third of a year or 4 months as the length of time for which the \$1000 is borrowed.

The formula $I = prt$ becomes $r = \frac{I}{pt}$ when solved for r. Suppose we have agreed to pay \$40 interest on \$2000, which we have borrowed for 6 months. Find the interest rate we are paying. Here $I = \$40$, $p = \$2000$, and $t = 6$ months.

Now $r = \frac{40}{(2000)(\frac{1}{2})} = \frac{4\cancel{0}}{100\cancel{0}} = 0.04$ or 4%, which is the rate of interest we are paying.

The formula $D = snd$ is another important one. Let us examine a situation in which it applies. Suppose you want to borrow \$600 for 3 months from a bank that charges 8%. Banks and other lending agencies usually *charge interest in advance.* This means that the bank will not hand you a check for \$600 which is the amount you asked to borrow. Instead they take 8% of \$600 for 3 months.

$\frac{8}{\cancel{100}} \times \overset{6}{\cancel{600}} = \$48$, the interest for one year. Three months equals ¼ of a year.

$$\frac{1}{\cancel{4}} \times \overset{12}{\cancel{\$48}} = \$12$$

This is the interest on \$600 for 3 months at 8%. The bank gives you \$588. Three months later you will be expected to pay the bank \$600. Thus the bank is actually charging *interest in advance*. *Bank Discount* is a business term for *interest in advance.*

Let us apply the formula $D = snd$ to the problem of borrowing \$600 for 3 months from a bank that charges 8%. In this formula s represents the sum to be borrowed, in this case \$600; n represents the time (*in years*), and d represents the discount rate (interest rate). Thus $n = \frac{1}{4}$ and $d = 0.08$. D equals the bank discount.

Now:

$$D = \left(\overset{6}{\cancel{600}}\right)\left(\frac{1}{\cancel{4}}\right)\left(\frac{\overset{2}{\cancel{8}}}{\cancel{100}}\right) = \$12, \text{ which is the bank discount.}$$

As pointed out previously the bank pays out \$588 in the loan transaction but expects to be paid back \$600. In charging interest in advance, the bank actually collects a higher rate of interest than appears in the terms of loan.

We shall now take the same situation as before. Assume that we want to borrow \$600 for 3 months from a bank that charges 8%. The sum of money we actually receive from the bank is \$588. The amount of interest we pay is \$12. Let us find the interest rate which is being charged.

Using $r = \frac{I}{pt}$, we have

$$r = \frac{12}{(588)(\frac{1}{4})} = \frac{12}{\frac{588}{4}} = \frac{48}{588}$$

$$= 0.0816 \text{ or } 8.2\%, \text{ whereas the charge stated in the loan was } 8\%.$$

The policy of bank discount should be thoroughly understood by all who borrow money.

Ordinary and exact interest. In computing interest when the time is given in months, we take each month as $1/12$ of a year. If the time is given in days, we may take each day to be $1/365$ of a year as there are 365 days in a year. It is frequently more convenient, however, and in most business transactions it is the custom, to consider a day as $1/360$ of a year. Actually, the denominator 365 being larger than the denominator 360, results in a smaller interest payment being made to the lender when 365 is used. Naturally the 360-day base is preferred by those who lend money.

Interest computed on the basis of a 360-day year is called *ordinary interest.* Interest computed on the basis of 365 days to the year is called *exact interest.* We shall use *ordinary interest* in all computations in this text involving simple interest.

Frequently in working with financial problems we find the time is not given as a number of days or months but we are asked to find the interest on a given principal from one date to another, say from June 12, 1960 to October 15, 1960. There are two methods we can use to find the time. One is the method of *approximate time.* The method of approximate time works on the basis of 30 days to the month or 360 days to the year. Let us find the approximate time between June 12, 1960 and October 15, 1960.

	Year	Month	Day
October 15, 1960 =	1960	10	15
June 12, 1960 =	1960	6	12
Subtracting, we find:		4	3

Four months and 3 days or 123 days is the approximate time between June 12, 1960 and October 15, 1960.

The method of *exact time* is based on the exact number of days in each month. Thus the total number of days in a year is 365, except in leap years when there are 366.

Let us find the exact time between June 12, 1960 and October 15, 1960. There are 18 days left in June, 31 in July, 31 in August, 30 in September, and 15 in October. This total gives us 125 days. Notice that we counted the last day but not the first one. Also observe that by the method of *approximate time* we found 123 days between June 12, 1960 and October 15, 1960, whereas by the method of *exact time* we found 125 days. A person lending money is consequently smart to use *ordinary interest and exact time.*

For example, Jack Jones borrows \$5000 from Harry Schmidt on April 16, 1961 and agrees to pay it back with 8% interest on November 19, 1961. Find how much Jones owes Schmidt on November 19, 1961. We shall compute this sum on the basis of *ordinary interest* and *exact time.* We use $I = prt$ or

$$I = p \times r \times \frac{\text{exact time between dates}}{360}$$

We shall now find the exact time between April 16, 1961 and November 19, 1961. From April 16 to April 30 is 14 days. May has 31 days; June 30; July 31; August 31; September 30; October 31; and November 19. The total is 217 days.

Now:

$$I = \overset{50}{\cancel{5000}} \times \frac{\overset{2}{\cancel{8}}}{\cancel{100}} \times \frac{217}{\underset{9}{\cancel{360}}}$$

$I =$ \$241.11, the amount of interest Jones owes Schmidt.

Jones also owes the \$5000 principal he has borrowed. A convenient relationship is $A = P + I$, or amount equals principal plus interest. Now Jones owes Schmidt \$5000 + \$241.11, or \$5241.11.

EXERCISE 4

In the following time periods find the approximate time between dates.

1. January 25, 1960 and April 14, 1960
2. February 10, 1959 and June 25, 1959
3. April 21, 1961 and September 26, 1961
4. July 16, 1961 and November 18, 1961
5. February 23, 1962 and December 24, 1962
6. March 24, 1962 and January 25, 1963
7. June 21, 1962 and March 18, 1963

8. July 30, 1962 and October 28, 1962

In the following find the exact time between dates.

9. October 18, 1962 and February 21, 1963
10. July 20, 1961 and November 24, 1961
11. May 14, 1962 and January 15, 1963
12. September 27, 1960 and March 15, 1961
13. April 19, 1961 and December 28, 1961
14. August 16, 1964 and March 19, 1965
15. October 25, 1959 and August 28, 1960
16. November 27, 1960 and September 24, 1961

In problems 17 through 24 find the ordinary interest for the exact time.

17. Principal $600, rate 7%, January 24, 1960 to July 27, 1960.

18. Principal $1300, rate 8%, March 26, 1960 to August 24, 1960.

19. Principal $260, rate 6½%, June 25, 1959 to October 4, 1959.

20. Principal $2340, rate 8¾%, August 15, 1960 to June 17, 1961.

21. Principal $1860, rate 9%, June 16, 1960 to April 24, 1961.

22. Principal $2240, rate 7¼%, 5 months.

23. Principal $36,000, rate 3½%, 60 days.

24. Principal $19,000, rate 2%, 30 days.

25. How long will it take the interest on $2600 at 3% to amount to $26.60?

26. How long will it take the interest on $3800 at 3½% to amount to $45.75?

27. At what rate will the interest on $1500 for 80 days be $12.40?

28. At what rate will the interest on $2600 for 125 days be $25.30?

29. The interest on a certain sum for 90 days at 4½% was $18.00. Find the sum.

30. What principal will amount to $1643.85 in 75 days at 3½%?

31. What principal will amount to $4500 in 90 days at 4%?

32. Will Winkle borrows $1500 from a bank whose discount rate is 7%. If he gives the bank a 90-day note, how much money does he receive from the bank? How much does he repay the bank at the end of the 90 days?

33. Ruth Roberts borrows $1800 from a bank whose discount rate is 8%. If she gives the bank a 120-day note, how much money does she receive from the bank? How much does she repay the bank at the end of the 120 days?

34. Roy Fish went to the Second National Bank and signed a 90-day note with face value $3500. Interest in advance at 6½% was deducted. How much did Fish receive on the loan? How much does he pay the Second National Bank at the end of 90 days?

35. Flossie Fleece needs to have $625 in order to pay a bill. What sum should Miss Fleece arrange to borrow from the bank if the bank charges interest in advance at 7% and the loan is to be repaid in 60 days?

5. PERIMETER AND CIRCUMFERENCE FORMULAS

The words perimeter and circumference both refer to distance around. However, perimeter refers to the distance around a closed broken line in a plane. Such a figure has examples in the triangle, square, and rectangle. A *triangle* is a figure formed in a plane by connecting three points that are not in a straight line.

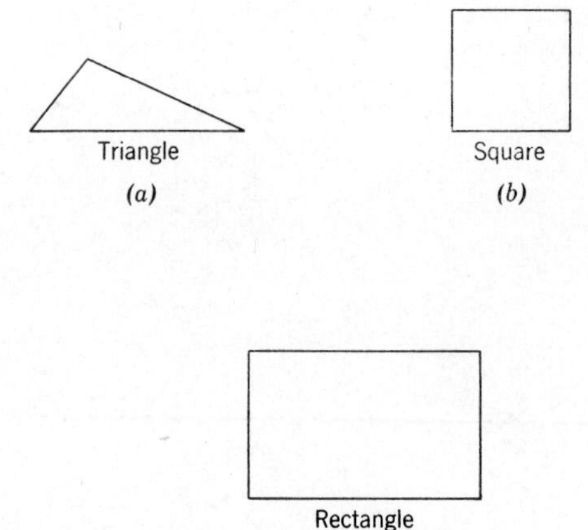

Figure 4

A *square* is a closed four-sided figure in a plane. A square has equal sides and equal angles. A *rectangle* is a closed four-sided figure in a plane. All the angles of a rectangle are right angles and all the angles of a square are right angles. How then, does a rectangle differ from a square?

Circumference refers to the distance around a circle or the length of the curved line which is the circle. While we could speak of the perimeter of a circle this generally is not done.

The perimeter of a closed broken line in a plane is the sum of the lengths of its sides. Thus if we let p stand for perimeter and let a, b, and c refer to the sides of a triangle, then $p = a + b + c$.

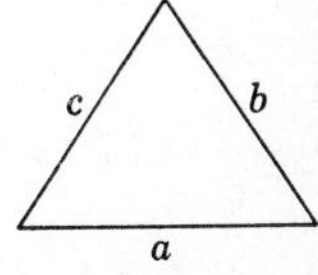

Figure 5

For example, find the perimeter of a triangle if the sides are 12.4 feet, 6.8 feet, and 14.5 feet. Assuming all measurements are approximate, we have $p = 12.4 + 6.8 + 14.5$ or 33.7 feet.

You may work out your own set of experiments to determine how many times the diameter of a circle is contained in the circumference. The objects used should be sufficiently large to give reasonably correct answers. Experiments with larger and smaller objects generally lead to the conclusion that better results are obtained if the object used is not too small and is carefully made. A circular table, earthen pipe, large crock, dinner plate, pan, or automobile tire, all furnish ample material for this kind of work. Through these experiments, the length of the diameter and circumference are obtained, and you will find that, regardless of the size of the circle used, the quotient of the circumference divided by the diameter is approximately the value 3.1416. This number is represented by the Greek letter π (read pī). It has been mathematically proved that the value of π cannot be expressed exactly as a whole number or as a combination of whole number and fraction. Mathematicians call it a *transcendental* number.

The circumference of a circle equals two times pi times the radius, or $2\pi r$. Since the radius of a circle is half the diameter, the circumference also may be written πd. Let us use π as 3.1416. Of course this is an approximate number. Diameter and radius measurements should also be considered as approximate numbers.

For example, find the circumference of a circle whose radius is 8.75 inches. Now $C = 2\pi r$ or $C = 2(3.1416)(8.75) = 55.0$ inches.

EXERCISE 5

Find the perimeters of the following figures.

1. A triangle whose sides are 25.6 feet, 31.2 feet, and 15.9 feet.

2. A rectangle two of whose sides are 125.4 yards and 68.9 yards.

3. A square whose side is 23.8 feet.

4. A triangle with one side 16.5 rods and the two other sides each equal to 33.8 yards.

5. A rectangle two of whose sides are 58.75 inches and 16.4 inches.

6. If l represents the length of a rectangle, and w its width, write a formula for its perimeter, p.

7. If s represents the side of a square, write a formula for its perimeter, p.

8. Find the circumference of a circle if its radius is 25.75 inches.

9. Find the circumference of a circle if its radius is 46.8 feet.

10. Find the circumference of a circle if its diameter is 124.5 yards.

11. Find the circumference of a circle if its diameter is $21\frac{1}{4}$ inches.

12. Find the perimeter of a rectangle if its length is 5.34 and its width is 4.7.

13. What is the circumference of a circle whose diameter is 5.38 inches?

14. What is the perimeter, p, of a semicircle whose radius is r?

15. The perimeter of a rectangle is 120 feet, and the length is twice the width. What are its dimensions?

16. The length of a rectangle is $3\frac{1}{2}$ times the width, and the perimeter is 54 feet. What are the dimensions?

17. Two sides of a triangle are equal in length, and the third side is 8 less than the length of the equal sides. If the perimeter of the triangle is 139, what are its sides?

18. The length of a rectangle is 9 less than four times the width, and the perimeter is 52. Find the dimensions.

19. A side of the larger of two squares is three times a side of

the smaller, and the sum of the perimeters of the two squares is 192. Find the sides of the two squares.

20. The length of a rectangle is 60% longer than the width. If the perimeter of the rectangle is 416 inches, what are its dimensions?

6. AREA FORMULAS FOR THE RECTANGLE, PARALLELOGRAM, AND TRIANGLE

The formula for the area of the rectangle is based upon direct measurement. In measuring the area of a rectangle let us use a square as a convenient unit of measure. To measure the area of the rectangle we find the number of times the rectangle contains the square. Consider a rectangle 6 centimeters long and 3 centimeters wide, and assume the unit of measure to be a square centimeter as in Figure 6. We see that the square is contained in the given rectangle 18 times. This fact is obtained very quickly by observing that in each row there are 6 of the square centimeters. Since there are 3 rows, the total number of square centimeters in the given rectangle is 6×3, or 18 square centimeters. We notice that the number of squares in each row is exactly equal to the number of linear units in the length of the rectangle, and the number of rows is equal to the number of linear units in the width of the rectangle. The rule for finding the area of a rectangle is as follows: The area of a rectangle is equal to the product of the number of units of length and the number of units of width. The result is units of area, or square units. For practical purposes we find it more convenient in computing areas of rectangles to use the formula $A = L \times W$. This statement says in words, of course, the area of a rectangle is equal to the product of the length and the width.

For example, find the area of a rectangle if its length is 8 feet and its width is 5 feet. In this illustration, $L = 8$ feet and $W =$ 5 feet. Then $A = 8 \times 5$, or 40 square feet. As we have commented before, it is very important that units be placed in the answer in a form consistent with the way they appear in the given problem. Thus in the illustration above, feet are given in the problem and the answer is expressed in square feet.

Consider now the parallelogram $ABCD$ in Figure 7. A *parallelogram* is a closed four-sided figure in a plane. A *parallelogram* has its opposite sides *parallel*. *Parallel* lines are lines which are equidistant apart. In Figure 7, AB and DC are parallel lines, and AD and BC are parallel lines. The line AB on which the parallelogram appears to be standing is called the base of the parallelogram. The shortest distance BE from the base AB to the opposite side DC is called the height of the parallelogram. If we take away the right triangle* BEC and consider it as placed on the left where triangle AFD is shown, a rectangle is made having the same base, height, and area as the original parallelogram. Hence, the number of units of area in a parallelogram is equal to the product of the number of units of length in the base and the number of units of length in the height. Expressing this idea simply as a formula we have, $A = b \times h$.

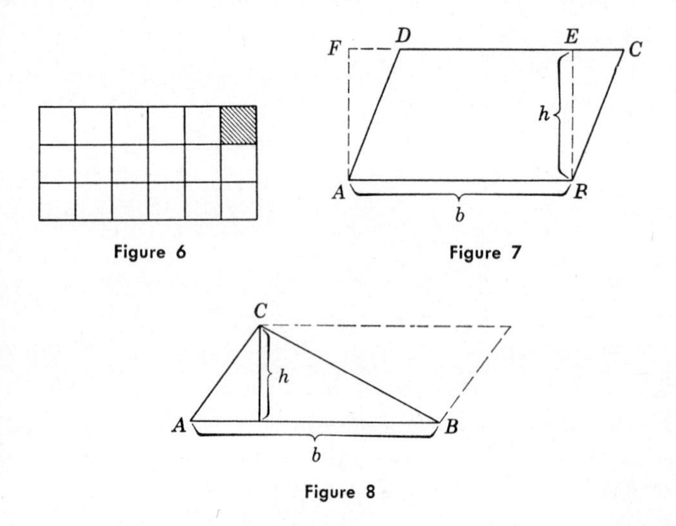

Figure 6 Figure 7

Figure 8

As an illustration, find the area of a parallelogram, the base of which is 18 inches and the height 5 inches. Here, $b = 18$ inches and $h = 5$ inches. Then $A = 18$ inches $\times$ 5 inches $= 90$ square inches.

Turning now to the finding of the area of a triangle, let us examine triangle ABC in Figure 8. We assume that ABC is a completely general triangle. If another triangle exactly the same size as ABC is located as indicated by dotted lines in Figure 8, a parallelogram appears. We see then that the area of a triangle is

* A right triangle is a triangle that contains a right angle. A right angle equals 90 degrees.

one-half the area of the parallelogram having the same base and height. Thus $A = \frac{1}{2} \times b \times h$. Now, find the area of a triangle whose base is 18 feet and whose height or altitude is 4.5 feet. An altitude of a triangle is the perpendicular distance from a vertex to the opposite side. In this example, $b = 18$ feet and $h =$ 4.5 feet. Then $A = \frac{1}{2} \times 18 \text{ feet} \times 4.5 \text{ feet}$, or 40.5 square feet. However, remembering that measurements are approximate numbers and following the rules explained in Chapter seven on approximate numbers, we round this result to 40 square feet.

EXERCISE 6

1. Find the area of the rectangle having the dimensions 17.4 feet by 6.9 feet.

2. Find the area of a rectangle which is 8.3 inches long and 6.9 inches wide.

3. A triangle has a base 124 feet long and an altitude of 75 feet. Find its area.

4. Find the area of a triangle if its base is 82 inches and its height is 31 inches.

5. Find the area of a parallelogram if its base is 64 inches and its height is 41 inches.

6. A parallelogram has a base of 23.5 feet and an altitude of 14.6 feet. Find its area.

7. Find the area of a rectangle 38 inches by 3.4 feet.

8. A rectangular field is 1924 feet long and 1232 feet wide. How many acres does the field contain?

9. A piece of land one mile square is known as a section. How many acres are there in a section?

10. How many bricks will be used in paving a street 35 feet wide and 4.6 miles long? Assume $7\frac{1}{2}$ bricks are needed per square foot.

11. Assuming that in planning a schoolroom, 15 square feet are used as the recommended floor space for each pupil, how many students will a room 24 feet by 38 feet house?

12. Laths are sold in bundles of 100. They are 4 feet long, approximately $1\frac{3}{8}$ inches wide, and are generally nailed on about $\frac{3}{8}$ of an inch apart. How many square yards of wall can be covered with a bundle?

13. Find the number of bundles of laths that will be needed to lath the walls and ceiling of a room 24 feet long, 16 feet wide, and 9 feet high?

14. A room is 16 feet wide and 24 feet long. How much will it cost to cover the floor of the room with linoleum if the linoleum costs $4 per square yard?

15. A room is 19 feet long and 15 feet wide. A rug is on the floor and the dimensions of this rug are 15 by 11 feet. How many square feet of floor space are not covered by the rug?

16. If two parallelograms have the same base, 16 inches, and altitudes of 12 inches and 6 inches, respectively, how do their areas compare?

17. The flight deck of a carrier is 9.03 times as long as it is wide. Find its width if its length is 832 feet.

18. Find the area in square yards of the flight deck in the problem above.

19. Aircraft plywood comes in sheets 48 by 72 inches. Find the price per square foot if it sells for $9.20 per sheet.

20. One triangle has a base of 22 inches and a height of 12 inches. A second triangle has a base of 11 inches. How high should it be in order to have an area which will be twice that of the first triangle?

7. AREA FORMULA FOR THE TRAPEZOID

The rule for finding the area of a trapezoid comes easily from

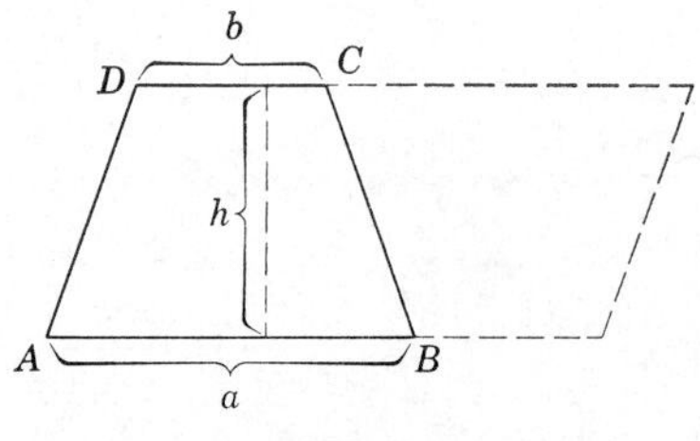

Figure 9

a study of Figure 9. Let $ABCD$ represent any trapezoid with a and b the lengths of the parallel sides. The area of the trapezoid is one-half the area of a parallelogram having the same height, but its base is equal to the sum of the lengths of the parallel sides of the trapezoid. Written as a formula, this is, $A = \frac{1}{2}h(a + b)$.

For example, find the area of a trapezoid whose bases are 22 and 12 inches respectively, and whose height is 15 inches. Here we have $a = 22$ inches, $b = 12$ inches, and $h = 15$ inches. Then:

$$A = \frac{1}{2}(15)(22 + 12) \text{ or } A = \frac{1}{2}(15)(34)$$

Finally, $A = 260$ square inches, rounding to two significant figures.

EXERCISE 7

Find the areas of the trapezoids in problems 1 through 10.

1. The bases are 8 and 6, and the altitude is 7.

2. The bases are 20 and 12, and the altitude is 6.

3. The bases are 324 feet and 62 feet, and the altitude is 46 feet.

4. The bases are 74 yards and 28 yards, and the altitude is 45 feet.

5. The bases are 9.2 centimeters and 6.8 centimeters, and the altitude is 4.7 centimeters.

6. The bases are 28.7 meters and 14.3 meters, and the altitude is 16.9 meters.

7. The bases are 124.3 kilometers and 83.6 kilometers, and the altitude is 20.8 meters.

8. The bases are 84.6 rods and 169.3 rods, and the altitude is 66.7 rods.

9. The bases are $123\frac{1}{2}$ inches and 17 feet, and the altitude is 68 inches.

10. The bases are 24.3 miles and 16.7 miles, and the altitude is 3960 feet.

11. In trapezoid $ABCD$ draw diagonal AC dividing the trapezoid into two triangles. Using the formula for finding the area of a triangle, develop the formula for finding the area of a trapezoid.

12. Find the formula for the area of Figure 10.

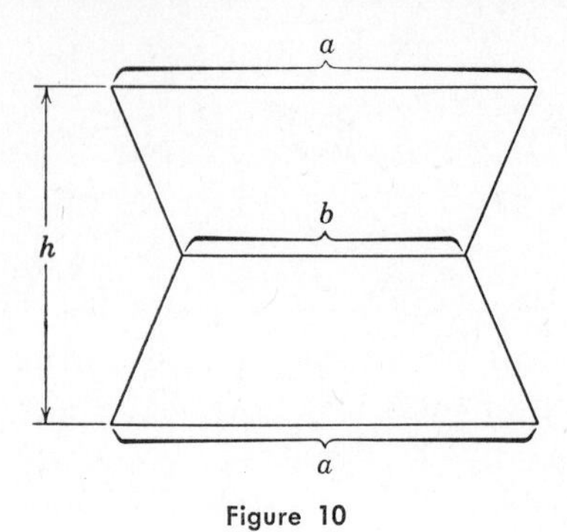

Figure 10

13. Find this area if $a = 23$ inches, $b = 18$ inches and $h = 32$ inches.

14. A city park in the shape of a trapezoid has its two parallel sides 330 feet and 282 feet, and it is 275 feet deep. How many acres does it contain?

15. The area of a trapezoid is 684 square feet. Its parallel bases are 224 feet and 135 feet respectively. What is the height of the trapezoid?

8. SQUARE ROOT

Let us think first about finding the squares of numbers. Two squared, or 2×2, or 2^2 equals 4. Five squared, or 5×5, or 5^2 equals 25. In finding the square root of a number we are actually determining what smaller value, when multiplied by itself, will equal this number. Thus 6 is the square root of 36, and 12 is the square root of 144.

Let us consider the following examples:

(a)	(b)	(c)
$1^2 = 1$	$10^2 = 100$	$100^2 = 10000$
$2^2 = 4$	$14^2 = 196$	$225^2 = 50625$
$5^2 = 25$	$23^2 = 529$	$669^2 = 447561$
$7^2 = 49$	$76^2 = 5776$	$853^2 = 727609$
$9^2 = 81$	$94^2 = 8836$	$966^2 = 933156$

(*d*)

$$0.1^2 = 0.\overset{\frown}{01}$$
$$0.4^2 = 0.\overset{\frown}{16}$$
$$2.3^2 = \overset{\frown}{5}.\overset{\frown}{29}$$
$$3.7^2 = \overset{\frown}{13}.\overset{\frown}{69}$$
$$10.29^2 = \overset{\frown}{1}\overset{\frown}{05}.\overset{\frown}{88}\overset{\frown}{41}$$

In column *a* we observe that the square root of a one- or two-digit number is in units, or is one place to the left of the decimal point. In column *b* we see that the square root of a three- or four-digit number is in tens, or two places to the left of the decimal point. In column *c* we find that the square root of a five- or six-digit number is in hundreds, or three places to the left of the decimal point. In column *d* we see that the square root of numbers one or two places to the right of the decimal is in tenths; the square root of numbers three or four places to the right of the decimal is in hundredths, and so forth.

In taking the square root of a number we pair off the digits to the left and the right of the decimal point in the number the square root of which is to be found. For example, to find the square root of 4, 196, 1936, 95481, 6342.7, and 85.4362 we have

$$4 = \overset{\frown}{4};\ \sqrt{4} \text{ will be in one digit}$$
$$196 = \overset{\frown}{1}\overset{\frown}{96};\ \sqrt{196} \text{ will be in two digits}$$
$$1936 = \overset{\frown}{19}\overset{\frown}{36};\ \sqrt{1936} \text{ will be in two digits}$$
$$95481 = \overset{\frown}{9}\overset{\frown}{54}\overset{\frown}{81};\ \sqrt{95481} \text{ will be in three digits}$$
$$6342.7 = \overset{\frown}{63}\overset{\frown}{42}.\overset{\frown}{7};\ \sqrt{6342.7} \text{ will be in two digits and one decimal place}$$
$$85.4362 = \overset{\frown}{85}.\overset{\frown}{43}\overset{\frown}{62};\ \sqrt{85.4362} \text{ will be in one digit and two decimal places}$$

For example, find the square root of 3136.

(1) Point off the digits in pairs, placing the decimal point above the line immediately above its position in the problem. $\sqrt{\overset{\frown}{31}\overset{\frown}{36}.}$

(2) Find the largest square contained in 31, the first grouping. Here $5 \times 5 = 25$, is the largest perfect square contained in 31. The number is 5; place it in the answer just above the 1 in 31.

```
                5 6.
             √ 3136.
               25
        100 |   636
          6 |
        ----|
        106 |   636
```

(3) Square the 5, which is the only number in the answer thus far, obtaining 25. Subtract this from 31. This gives 6.

(4) Bring down the next group of two digits, 36.

(5) Double the answer thus far obtained, $2 \times 5 = 10$. Annex one zero to the 10, making it 100. Use this as a trial divisor. Thus 636 divided by 100 will give approximately 6. Add 6 to the trial divisor, 100 plus 6 equals 106. Place 6 in the answer just above the 6 in 36. Multiply the 106 by 6. This gives 636.

(6) Subtract 636. Since there is no remainder, 3136 is the perfect square of 56. If the number 3136 were not a perfect square, we would need to annex two zeros at a time and continue the process of solution until the desired degree of accuracy had been reached.

In examining square roots of approximate numbers we make an observation. The square of the approximate number 16.8, when rounded according to rules for multiplying approximate numbers, is 282. In taking the square root of 282 we find 16.8. *The square root of a number contains the same number of significant digits as the given number.* Thus to find the square root of an approximate number with x number of significant digits, carry the answer to $x + 1$ significant digits, and round the answer one place.

As another example, find the square root of 7.34, and assume it to be an approximate number.

```
          2. 7 0 9     which rounds to 2.71 for the answer
        √ 7.340000
          4
40    |   3 34
 7    |
------|
47    |   3 29
5400  |      50000
   9  |
------|
5409  |      48681
```

9. THE PYTHAGOREAN THEOREM AND SOME OF ITS APPLICATIONS

In a right triangle the side opposite the right angle is the *hypotenuse,* whereas the other two sides are the *legs.* These names are not given to the sides of any other kind of triangle.

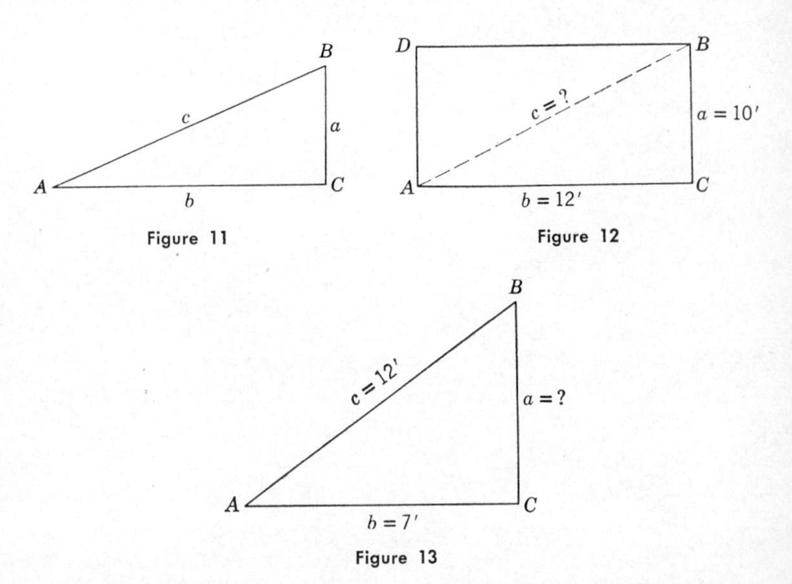

Figure 11

Figure 12

Figure 13

The right triangle is conventionally labeled as shown in Figure 11. The capital letters A, B, and C designate the angles, C always indicating the right angle. The small (lower case) letters a, b, c represent the sides opposite the angles A, B, and C, respectively. Of course c is always the hypotenuse; a, the leg opposite angle A; and b, the leg opposite angle B. With respect to angle A, a is known as the opposite leg and b, the leg adjacent. Of course the adjectives are reversed with respect to angle B, since b stands for the opposite leg and a for the adjacent leg.

The distinctive property of the right triangle is expressed algebraically in the equation $c^2 = a^2 + b^2$ and by the equivalent equations $a^2 = c^2 - b^2$ and $b^2 = c^2 - a^2$. This property is expressed geometrically in the famous theorem of Pythagoras which states that the area of the square whose side is c equals the sum of the areas of the squares whose sides are a and b.

Example 1: If the sides of a rectangle are 10 feet and 12 feet, how long is a diagonal of the rectangle? In many instances a figure is desirable in understanding a problem.

In Figure 12 we have rectangle $ACBD$ with diagonal c and right triangle ACB with hypotenuse c and sides a and b. From the Pythagorean Theorem we have $c^2 = a^2 + b^2$.

Substituting from the figure we have

$c^2 = (10)^2 + (12)^2$, or
$c = \sqrt{100 + 144}$
$c = \sqrt{244}$ or 15.6 feet
$c = 16$ feet, rounding according to approximate numbers.

Example 2: If a ladder 12 feet long rests against a wall, with the foot of the ladder 7 feet from the foot of the wall, how high up on the wall is the top of the ladder?

We can clear this problem up rather nicely with the help of a diagram.

In Figure 13 we see that $c = 12$ feet and $b = 7$ feet. But $c^2 = a^2 + b^2$, and $a^2 = c^2 - b^2$. Then

$a^2 = (12)^2 - (7)^2$, or
$a = \sqrt{144 - 49}$
$a = \sqrt{95} = 9.75$ or 10 feet where the zero is not significant.

This tells how high up on the wall the ladder reaches.

EXERCISE 8

Find the square roots of the following 20 problems, assuming the numbers given in each case are approximate numbers. The answers should be rounded accordingly.

1. 49
2. 81
3. 4356
4. 7225
5. 171.61
6. 134.56
7. 17.3889
8. 18.4041
9. 134.6
10. 45.62
11. 6003.8
12. 513.9
13. 7892.6
14. 86.579
15. 124.662
16. 3462.8
17. 0.0063
18. 0.00064
19. 0.01694
20. 0.07536

21. Find the side of a square whose area is 289 square feet.

22. Find the side of a square whose area is 324 square centimeters.

23. A rope 82 feet long is attached to the top of a flagpole and reaches to a point on the ground 61 feet from the foot of the pole. How high is the pole?

24. The sides of a right triangle are 12 feet and 16 feet. Find the hypotenuse.

25. Find the length of a side of a square whose diagonal is 15 feet longer than a side.

26. If a tether ball swings on a rope 8 feet long, from the top of a pole 12 feet high, how far from the pole is the ball when it is at a level 7 feet above the ground?

27. Find the length of a rafter for a roof if its height is 12 feet and its span is 34 feet.

28. Find the altitude of an isosceles triangle if the equal sides are 9 inches and the base is 6 inches. An isosceles triangle is a triangle with two equal sides.

29. Find the length of the diagonal of a rectangular box having dimensions of 6 feet, 5 feet, and 4 feet.

30. During a storm, a tree 48 feet high snaps so that the upper portion, which still remains attached to the trunk where it snapped, touches the ground 24 feet from the foot of the tree. How high up is the break in the tree?

10. AREA FORMULAS FOR CIRCLE AND ELLIPSE

A circle is a closed curve every point of which is equally distant from a point within, called the center. If r is the radius of a given circle, its area is given by the formula $A = \pi r^2$. Here π is a number which can never be expressed exactly as a common or decimal fraction. It is equal to $22/7$ or 3.14159, both of which are approximate values.

For example, find the area of a circle whose radius is 23.5 inches. Let us use π here as 3.14, carrying the same number of digits as we have in the radius. Now since $A = \pi r^2$, $A = 3.14(23.5)^2$, or $A = 3.14(552.2)$, when we round the $(23.5)^2$ to four significant figures (one more than we expect to use in the answer). Then $A = 1730$ square inches.

The ellipse is a beautiful figure rather frequently used in designs. Elliptical gears and cams are frequently used in machinery. Elliptical arches often appear in bridges and on the paneling in furniture. Furthermore, each planet moves in an ellipse, although until the time of the astronomer Kepler (1571–1630) it was thought that the planets moved in circles.

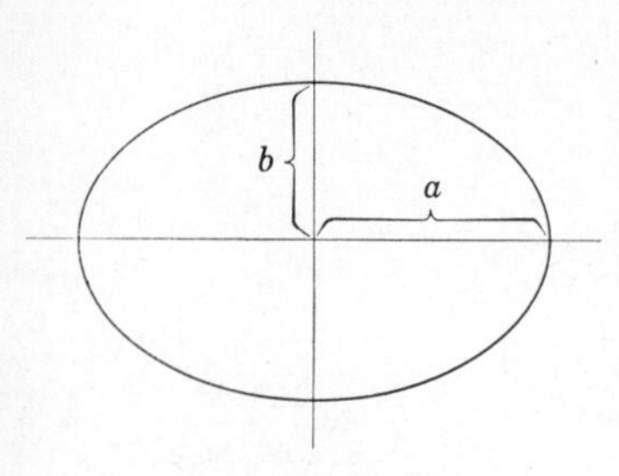

Figure 14

In the ellipse, the long diameter is called the *major axis* and the short diameter is called the *minor axis*. In Figure 14 an ellipse is shown; a is called the semi-major axis and b, the semi-minor axis.

The area of an ellipse is πab or π times the semi-major axis times the semi-minor axis. This formula is $A = \pi ab$.

For example, find the area of the ellipse whose semi-major axis is 24.2 inches and whose semi-minor axis is 16.5 inches. Let us use 3.14 for π, keeping a consistent number of significant figures. Now $A = (3.14)(24.2)(16.5)$, or $A = (3.14)(399.3)$. Then $A = 1250$ square inches. Here the zero is not significant, of course.

EXERCISE 9

Find the areas of the following circles. In each case round π to a consistent number of significant figures using $\pi = 3.14159$ as an approximate value from which to start the rounding.

1. Radius = 6 inches
2. Radius = 10 inches
3. Radius = 25.2 meters
4. Radius = 64.3 centimeters
5. Radius = 65.3 feet
6. Radius = 85.7 rods
7. Diameter = 84 inches
8. Diameter = 52 centimeters
9. Diameter = 124 kilometers
10. Diameter = 0.75 mile

Find the areas of the following ellipses, rounding as was suggested for the circles.

11. Semi-major axis 12; semi-minor axis 8
12. Semi-major axis 22; semi-minor axis 10
13. Semi-major axis 42 inches; semi-minor axis 21 inches

14. Semi-major axis 74 feet; semi-minor axis 38 feet

15. Semi-minor axis 124 kilometers; semi-major axis 382 kilometers

16. Semi-minor axis 24 rods; semi-major axis 126 rods

17. Semi-major axis 56 feet; semi-minor axis 40 inches

18. Semi-major axis 3468 meters; semi-minor axis 2364 centimeters

19. Find the area of the largest circle that can be cut from a 15-inch square.

20. In problem 19, the area of the circle is what per cent of the area of the square?

21. Find the formula for the area of a circular ring if r_1 is the radius of the outside circle and r_2 is the radius of the inside circle.

22. Find the cost of a sidewalk 6 feet wide around a circle whose diameter is 142 feet, if the cost is 52 cents a square foot.

23. Solve the formula $A = \pi r^2$ for r.

24. What is the radius of a circular tract that contains an acre?

25. What is the radius of a circle that has an area equal to that of a 12-foot square?

11. RATIO AND PROPORTION

A ratio is the quotient of two numbers expressed in like terms. Thus the ratio of 6 inches to 15 inches is $\frac{6 \text{ inches}}{15 \text{ inches}}$, which reduces to $\frac{2}{5}$. The fraction is always reduced to lowest terms and is expressed in abstract terms. That is, no units are expressed for a ratio in simplest form. If we are trying to express the ratio of 6 inches to 6 feet we do not have $\frac{6}{6} = 1$, because one of the units is inches and the other is feet. If we express both as inches, we have $\frac{6 \text{ inches}}{72 \text{ inches}} = \frac{1}{12}$. If we express both as feet, we have

$$\frac{\frac{1}{2}\text{ foot}}{6\text{ feet}} = \frac{1}{2} \times \frac{1}{6} = \frac{1}{12}$$

Always be sure that like units are compared in writing ratios. If we are asked to find the ratio between 6 inches and 8 gallons, we can say there is *no ratio* because these units cannot be changed to like terms.

A proportion is a statement that two ratios are equal. Thus $\frac{4}{8} = \frac{1}{2}$ is a proportion that may also be written in the form $4{:}8 = 1{:}2$. The first statement is read, "four over eight equals one over two," or "four-eighths equals one-half." The first and second statements may both be read, "four is to eight as one is to two."

For example, if a car can go 96.3 miles on 6.2 gallons of gasoline, how many miles can it go on 12 gallons of gasoline? Following the rules for approximate numbers, after setting up the proportion we have $\frac{96.3}{x} = \frac{6.2}{12}$. In this proportion, x represents the number of miles the car can travel on 12 gallons. Simplifying by multiplying both sides of the equation by $12x$, we have

$$12\cancel{x}\left(\frac{96.3}{\cancel{x}}\right) = \cancel{12}x\left(\frac{6.2}{\cancel{12}}\right)$$

Then:

$$\begin{aligned} 6.2x &= 12(96.3) \\ 6.2x &= 1155.6 \text{ or } 1160 \\ x &= 187 \text{ or } 190 \text{ miles, rounding} \\ &\quad \text{to two significant figures} \end{aligned}$$

EXERCISE 10

1. A college has 1824 students, 612 of whom are women. What is the ratio of men students to women students?

2. What is the ratio of 6 pints to 8 quarts?

3. What is the ratio of 8 inches to 24 feet?

4. Two boys divide 25 marbles in the ratio 4:1. How many marbles does each boy have?

5. A baseball team wins 4 games out of every 9 games it plays. Find the ratio of the games it wins to the games it plays.

6. In the above problem, find the ratio of the games won to the games lost.

7. Two girls divide $10.20 in the ratio of 3:2. How much does each girl receive?

8. Find the ratio of 20 centimeters to 100 meters.

9. A man hits a target 4 out of every 12 shots. What is the ratio of his hits to his misses?

10. What is the ratio of 6 quarts to 3 gallons?

11. What is the ratio of 4 pounds to 52 ounces?

12. What is the ratio of 3 miles to 5280 yards?

13. If a car can go 92 miles on 6.2 gallons of gasoline, how far can it go on 34 gallons of gasoline?

14. A car travels 88 feet per second. Find its speed in miles per hour.

15. A conveyor belt carries 21 cubic feet of coal per minute. How many cubic yards will be carried in 3.2 hours?

16. Change 840 gallons per hour into quarts per second.

17. A 100-pound bag of fertilizer contains 22 pounds of limestone. How many pounds of limestone will 73.4 pounds of fertilizer contain?

18. If 35 identical bolts weigh 3.4 pounds, how many pounds will 21 of these bolts weigh?

19. If 6.0 pounds of pecans sell for $2.40, how much will the selling price be for 9 pounds?

20. Using problem 19, how many pounds of pecans can be bought for $104?

21. Dress material is priced at 3.0 yards for $1.98. How much will $6\frac{1}{2}$ yards of the material cost?

22. A fertilizer mixture contains 2 parts nitrogen, 2 parts potash, and 3 parts phosphate by weight. How many pounds of the mixture will contain 40 pounds of potash?

23. A paving mixture contains 2 parts cement, 2 parts sand, and 3 parts gravel by weight. How many pounds of the mixture can be made with 2146 pounds of cement?

24. The volumes of similar solids are proportional to the cubes of corresponding dimensions. If the diagonal of a cube is tripled, what change is made in the volume?

25. The year's profits in a certain business were $24,000. Mr. Smith has $15,000, Mr. Jones has $20,000, and Mr. Baker has $25,000 invested in the business. If the profits were distributed according to each partner's investment, how much did each receive?

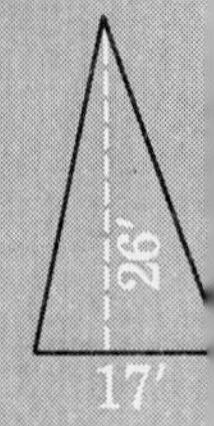

CHAPTER NINE

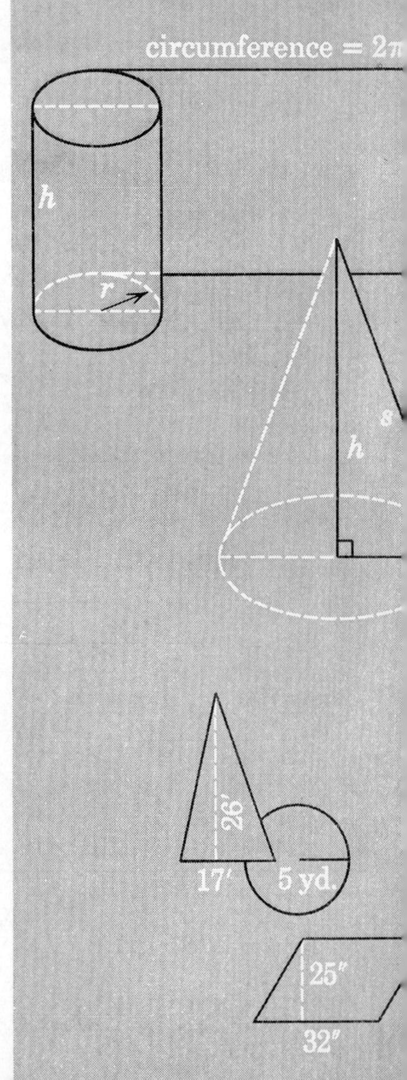

AREAS AND VOLUMES OF ELEMENTARY SOLIDS

1. RECTANGULAR SOLID AND PYRAMID

Geometric figures with three dimensions are called solids. These figures have length, width, and height or depth.

A rectangular solid is a figure that is formed by six rectangles that are parallel to each other in pairs. If the rectangles are squares, the rectangular solid formed is a cube.

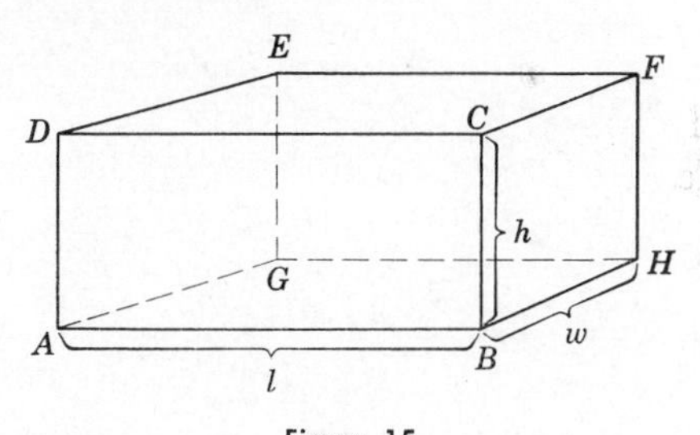

Figure 15

Figure 15 shows a rectangular solid. The rectangles *ABCD*, *BHFC*, *HFEG*, *AGED*, *ABHG*, and *DCFE* form the solid figure. If we let $l =$ the length of the rectangular solid, and let w and h be its width and height respectively, we can rather readily see the formula for the total surface area of the rectangular solid. The area of rectangle *ABCD* equals lh. The area of rectangle

BHFC is hw, and the area of rectangle *ABHG* is lw. Now, using the rectangles in all six surfaces we have area $= 2lw + 2hw + 2lh$, or $A = 2(lw + hw + lh)$, as the total surface area of a box with top and bottom.

Let us find the total surface area of a rectangular solid whose length measures 12.3 inches, whose width measures 6.4 inches, and whose height measures 5.7 inches. Then:

$$A = 2(12.3 \times 6.4 + 5.7 \times 6.4 + 12.3 \times 5.7).$$
$$A = 2(73.72 + 36.48 + 70.11)$$
$$A = 2(73.7 + 36.5 + 70.1)$$
$$A = 2(180.3) = 2(180) \text{ or } 360 \text{ square inches}$$

In measuring the volume of a solid we choose a unit of volume. We generally choose a cube whose edge is one linear unit in length. The most common units of volume are the cubic inch, cubic foot, or cubic centimeter.

The formula for the volume of the rectangular solid is $v = l \times w \times h$, in which $l =$ length, $w =$ width, $h =$ height.

Let us find the volume of a bin which is 6 feet long, 4 feet wide, and 3 feet deep. Here $v =$ (6 feet) (4 feet) (3 feet) $=$ (24 square feet) (3 feet) $=$ 72 cubic feet. Rounding, since we are working with approximate numbers, we obtain 70 cubic inches.

A pyramid is a solid whose base is a polygon and whose lateral surfaces are triangles with a common vertex, which is called the *vertex* of the pyramid. A polygon is a closed plane figure bounded by straight lines. A *vertex* of a triangle is the point of intersection of two sides of the triangle.

The altitude of a pyramid is the perpendicular distance from the vertex to the base. Figure 16 shows a pyramid in which *ABCD* is the base, and triangles *ABO, BCO, CDO,* and *ADO* are the lateral surfaces. *OP* is the altitude of the pyramid.

Of course the base of a pyramid may be any of the polygons. Those appearing most frequently as bases are the triangle, square, and rectangle.

The slant height of a pyramid is the perpendicular from the vertex to one edge of the base of a regular pyramid. Thus *OE* represents the slant height. In defining a *regular pyramid* we use the term *regular polygon.* A regular polygon is one all of whose sides are equal and all of whose angles are equal. If the base of a pyramid is a regular polygon and if the perpendicular from the vertex to the base passes through the center of the base, the pyramid is known as a *regular pyramid.*

The lateral surface of the pyramid refers to the sum of triangles ABO, BCO, CDO, and DAO in Figure 16. *The area of the*

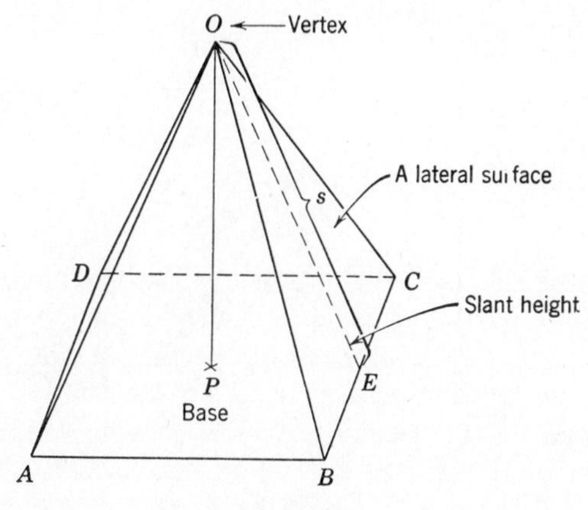

Figure 16

lateral surface of a regular pyramid equals one-half the product of the perimeter of the base and the slant height. Using the perimeter of the base as p and the slant height as s, we have A or area $= \frac{1}{2}ps$.

Find the lateral area of a regular pyramid whose slant height is 12.3 inches and the perimeter of whose base is 84.6 inches. Now $A = \frac{1}{2}(84.6)(12.3)$ or $A = (42.3)(12.3) = 520.29$ or 520 square inches.

The volume of a pyramid equals one third of the product of its altitude and its base. The formula here is $v = \frac{1}{3}Bh$, where B refers to the area of the base and h is the height.

Find the volume of the pyramid if its base is a 6-inch square and its altitude is 7 inches. Here the area of the base is 6 inches $\times$ 6 inches or 36 square inches. Then $v = \frac{1}{3}$(36 square inches) (7 inches) $= 84$ cubic inches or 80 cubic inches when rounded according to approximate numbers.

EXERCISE 1

1. Find the volume of a rectangular solid $3\frac{1}{4}$ inches by 5 inches by 4 inches.

2. Find the volume of a rectangular solid $3\frac{1}{2}$ feet by 6 feet by 5 feet.

3. A box is to be 12 inches long, and 6 inches wide. How deep must it be made to hold 600 cubic inches?

4. A rectangular solid is 8 inches wide and 15 inches long and contains 900 cubic inches. Find its height.

5. A bin 15.5 feet long and 9.4 feet wide is filled 6.2 feet deep with wheat. How many bushels of wheat are in the bin? Use 2150 cubic inches as a bushel.

6. A rectangular oil can has a square base, 10 inches by 10 inches, and is 15 inches deep. How many quarts will it hold?

7. A coal bin is 10 feet long, 8 feet wide, and 5 feet deep. Find how many tons the bin will hold if the coal weighs 52 pounds per cubic foot.

8. Find the cost of digging a cellar 40 feet long, 30 feet wide, and 8 feet deep at $1.70 per cubic yard.

9. How many bricks are necessary to pave a patio 35 feet wide and 50 feet long? Assume 7.5 bricks are needed per square foot.

10. How many bushels of potatoes can be stored in a bin 12 feet long, 9 feet wide, and 4 feet deep? A bushel of potatoes uses approximately 1.25 cubic feet.

11. A pyramid has a square base, 5 feet on each side, and an altitude of 3 feet. Find the volume of the pyramid.

12. Find the altitude of a pyramid whose volume is 400 cubic inches and whose base has an area of 81 square inches.

13. Find the number of square yards of canvas necessary to make a tent in the form of a pyramid whose slant height is 12 feet and whose base is 15 feet square. Allow 3 square yards extra for seams and waste.

14. If the base of a pyramid is a square 15 inches on a side, and the altitude is 10 inches, what is the volume?

15. A church steeple is in the shape of a regular pyramid whose base has 8 sides. If the slant height is 28.6 feet and an edge of the base is 6.3 feet, find the lateral area of the steeple.

16. A regular pyramid has a square base whose edge is 9.8 inches. The slant height is 16.4 inches. Find the lateral area of the pyramid.

17. Find the total area of the pyramid in problem 16.

18. A railroad tie is in the shape of a rectangular solid. It is 6 feet long, 8 inches wide, and 6 inches thick. The tie is to be dipped in creosote. What is the area of the treated surface?

19. How many square feet of copper are required to line the bottom and sides of a rectangular cistern, 10.3 feet long, 6.8 feet wide, and 4.3 feet deep?

20. Find the cost of building a stone wall 123 feet long, 5.3 feet high, and 1.5 feet thick at $3.50 a perch. One perch = 22 cubic feet approximately.

21–23. In problem 11, problem 12, and problem 14, preceding, use the Pythagorean Theorem to determine the slant height of each pyramid, and then find the total area of each pyramid.

24,25. In problem 13 and problem 16, use the Pythagorean Theorem to determine the altitude of each pyramid, and then find the volume of each pyramid.

2. CYLINDER

A cylinder is a very common geometric figure. Tanks and cans for various uses are frequently in the form of cylinders. If a rectangle is rotated about one side as an axis, the geometric solid formed is known as a right circular cylinder. The bases of the cylinder are circles. Each element of the curved surface is perpendicular to the bases. See Figure 17.

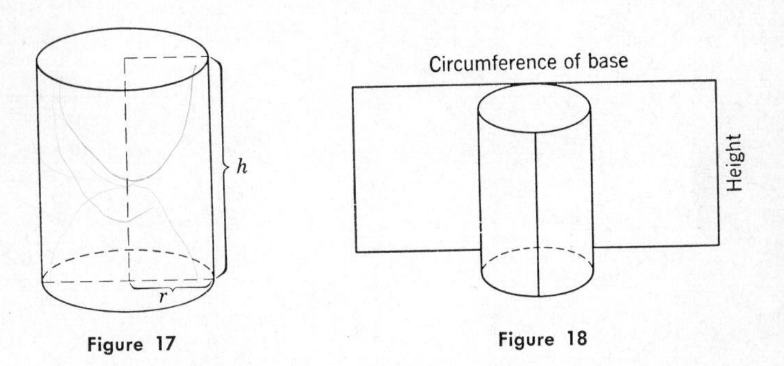

Figure 17 Figure 18

The volume of a circular cylinder equals π *times the square of the radius times the altitude.* Written as a formula this statement is $v = \pi r^2 h$.

The lateral surface of a right circular cylinder equals the area of a rectangle whose altitude is the altitude of the cylinder and whose base is the circumference of the cylinder. This fact can be shown by joining the ends of a rectangular sheet of paper and observing Figure 18.

The lateral area or curved surface of a right circular cylinder equals the product of the altitude and the circumference of the base. The formula for this relationship is $A = 2\pi rh$.

Find the lateral area and volume of a right circular cylinder the radius of whose base is 6.3 inches and whose height is 7.8 inches.

Now:
$$A = 2(3.14)(6.3)(7.8)$$
$$A = (6.28)(6.3)(7.8)$$
$$A = (39.6)(7.8)$$
$$A = 305.88 \text{ or } 310 \text{ square inches}$$

Also:
$$v = \pi r^2 h$$
$$v = (3.14)(6.3)^2(7.8)$$
$$v = (3.14)(39.7)(7.8)$$
$$v = (125)(7.8)$$
$$v = 980 \text{ cubic inches}$$

EXERCISE 2

1. Find the volume of the cylinder the radius of whose base is 8.4 inches and whose height is 12.6 inches.

2. Find the lateral area of the cylinder described in problem 1.

3. Write the formula for the total surface area of a right circular cylinder. We mean here the lateral surface plus the top and bottom.

4. Find the volume of a cylinder the radius of whose base is 10.3 feet and whose height is 14.7 feet.

5. Find the total surface area of the cylinder in problem 4.

6. A right circular cylinder has a diameter equal to 8.7 centimeters and a height equal to 12.8 centimeters. Find its volume.

7. If the cylinder in problem 6 has no top, find its total area.

8. Find the capacity in tons of a circular silo 19 feet in

diameter and 32 feet high, if 1 cubic foot of silage weighs 40.7 pounds.

9. The outside dimensions of a hollow cylindrical cast-iron shaft are: length 22 feet and diameter 24 inches. The inside diameter is 23 inches. Find the weight of the shaft if cast iron weighs 0.26 pound per cubic inch.

10. Hassocks are made in the form of right circular cylinders of diameter 28 inches and altitude 18 inches. What is the cost of construction if the leather covering costs $2.75 per square yard for the top and cylindrical surface, and $1.25 per square yard for the bottom? Other expenses will amount to 45 cents. Waste will amount to 12%.

11. Find the amount of lumber that will be needed for the lateral surface of a cylindrical silo 28 feet high and 14 feet in diameter.

12. What is the grinding surface of a grindstone that is 1½ feet in diameter and 3 inches thick?

13. How much paint will be needed for the lateral surface of a cylindrical silo whose diameter is 26 feet and whose height is 28 feet? Assume 1 gallon will cover approximately 250 square feet.

14. A lawn roller is made from a hollow iron cylinder whose inside diameter is 1.2 feet and whose length is 2.0 feet. If it weighs 28 pounds empty, what will it weigh when filled with water? Assume water weighs 62.5 pounds per cubic foot.

15. A cylindrical oil drum has a radius of 17 inches and a height of 38 inches. How many gallons does it hold?

3. CONE

If a right triangle is rotated about one side as an axis, a right circular cone is formed. Thus in Figure 19 triangle ACB is rotated about AC, forming the cone. The lateral area of the surface of a cone is all of the area except that of the base. The lateral area equals one-half the product of the circumference of the base and the slant height. Thus $L = \pi rs$, in which r is the radius of the

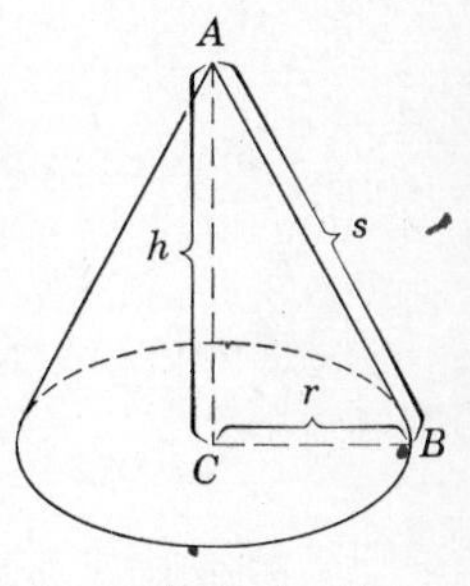

Figure 19

base, s the slant height, and L the lateral surface. Letting A be the total surface of the cone, we have $A = \pi rs + \pi r^2$ or $\pi r(s + r)$.

The volume of a cone equals one-third of the product of the area of the base of the cone and its altitude. The formula for volume is $v = \frac{1}{3}\pi r^2 h$, in which r again is the radius of the base and h is the altitude.

Find the total surface area of a cone the radius of whose base is 12.3 inches and whose slant height is 25.8 inches. Now:

$$A = \pi r(s + r) \text{ or } A = (3.14)(12.3)(25.8 + 12.3)$$

Then $A = (38.62)(38.1)$ or $A = 1470.$ square inches.

Now let us find the volume of the above cone. But:

$$v = \frac{1}{3}\pi r^2 h, \text{ or } v = \frac{1}{3}(3.14)(12.3)^2(25.8), \text{ or } v = \frac{1}{3}(3.14)(151.3)(25.8)$$

Now: $$v = \frac{1}{3}(3.14)(3904) \text{ or } v = \frac{1}{3}(12260.) = 4090 \text{ cubic inches}$$

EXERCISE 3

1. Find the volume of a cone, the radius of the base being $10\frac{3}{4}$ inches and the altitude $14\frac{3}{8}$ inches.

2. How many square yards of canvas are required to make a conical tent 9.5 feet in diameter and $8\frac{3}{4}$ feet high, allowing 3.5 square yards extra for seams and waste?

3. Find the number of cubic yards in a sand pile which is assumed to be a cone, if the cone is $9\frac{1}{4}$ feet in diameter and $4\frac{1}{2}$ feet high.

4. Find the formula for the radius of a cone when the volume and altitude are known.

5. Find the formula for the altitude of a cone when the volume and the radius of the base are given.

6. A right triangle with sides 35.6 inches and 21.4 inches is revolved about the longer side. Find the lateral area of the cone generated.

7. In the above problem find the total area of the cone.

8. Find the volume of the cone described in problem 6.

9. A buoy is composed of a right circular cylinder of diameter 4.3 feet and altitude 8.5 feet surmounted by a cone whose altitude is 6.7 feet. Find the surface of the entire buoy.

10. The total area of an equilateral cone is 65π square feet. Find the radius of the base of the cone.

11. The lateral area of a cone of revolution is 282π square centimeters, and the slant height is 32.4 centimeters. Find the altitude of the cone.

12. A right triangle, whose legs are 18 feet and 23 feet is revolved about its longer leg as an axis. Find the lateral surface of the cone thus formed.

13. The area of the base of a right circular cone is 1562 square inches, and the altitude of the cone is 18.7 inches. Find the slant height.

14. The radius of the base of a right circular cone is 9.4 feet, and the altitude is 12.3 feet. Find the total area of the cone.

15. Find the volume of the cone described in problem 14.

4. SPHERE

The word sphere comes from the Greek *sphaira,* meaning a ball. A sphere is a solid included by a closed surface every point of which is the same distance from a point within, called the center. Spheres are used very frequently in our highly mechanized age. As an example think of ball bearings in wheels.

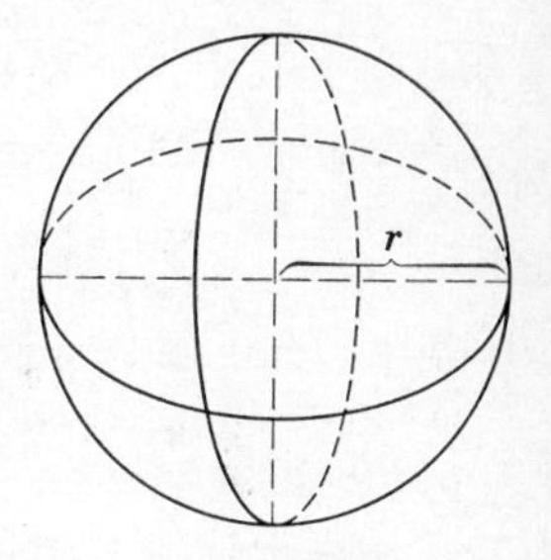

Figure 20

A sphere is shown in Figure 20. The volume of a sphere is found by multiplying four-thirds times pi times the cube of the radius. Written as a formula this statement is $v = \frac{4}{3}\pi r^3$. The surface area of a sphere is found by multiplying four times pi times the square of the radius. This formula is $S = 4\pi r^2$.

Find the volume of a sphere the radius of whose base is 0.125 of an inch.

$$v = \tfrac{4}{3}\pi r^3$$
$$v = \tfrac{4}{3}(3.142)(0.125)^3$$
$$v = \tfrac{4}{3}(3.142)(0.0020)$$
$$v = \tfrac{4}{3}(0.0063)$$
$$v = 0.008 \text{ cubic inch}$$

Find the surface of the above sphere.

$$S = 4\pi r^2$$
$$S = 4(3.142)\,(0.125)^2$$
$$S = 4(3.142)\,(0.0156)$$
$$S = 4(.0490) = 0.196 \text{ of a square inch}$$

EXERCISE 4

1. Find the area of a sphere with a radius of 16.4 inches.
2. Find the area of a sphere with a radius of 18.6 inches.
3. Find the volume of the sphere in problem 1.
4. Find the volume of the sphere in problem 2.
5. Find the volume of the sphere with radius 8.3 feet.
6. Find the volume of the sphere with radius 10.4 meters.
7. Find the area of the sphere in problem 5.
8. Find the area of the sphere in problem 6.
9. The geography department in a college has eight 10-inch globes. That is, the globes are 10 inches in diameter. Find the surface area of one of these globes.
10. The moon is 2160 miles in diameter. Find its surface area in square miles.
11. How much leather is needed to cover a basketball 10 inches in diameter? Allow 15% for seams and waste.
12. How many cubic feet of gas will a spherical storage tank hold if its inside diameter is 42 feet?
13. A capitol dome is a hemisphere 70 feet in diameter. How many squares of paint will be needed for two coats of paint? A square = 100 square feet.
14. If the radius of a sphere is doubled, what effect does this have on the volume?
15. If the radius of a sphere is multiplied by four, what effect does this have on the volume?
16. A lead sphere 6 inches in diameter is melted and converted into lead shot $\frac{1}{8}$ inch in diameter. Approximately how many pellets of shot will there be?
17. A malleable iron bar in the shape of a cylinder 3 feet long and 2 inches in diameter is drawn into iron wire $\frac{1}{16}$ inch in

diameter. About how much more than a half mile of wire will there be?

18. How many spherical shot 0.18 inch in diameter can be made from a cylindrical bar of metal 3 inches in diameter and 2 feet long?

19. Two spheres of radii 4 inches and 5 inches are melted and recast into a new sphere. Find the area of the new sphere.

20. How many balls $\frac{1}{8}$ inch in diameter can be made from a steel ball 8 inches in diameter?

EXERCISE 5

REVIEW

1. Find the length of the longest wire that can be stretched in a room that is 42 feet long, 36 feet wide, and 11 feet high.

2. Find the square root of 65.48.

3. Find the square root of 0.0893.

4. A chemist has two acid solutions; one is 60% acid and the other is 25% acid. How much of each should he take in order to have 125 cubic centimeters of acid solution which is 45% acid?

5. How much water should be added to 1 quart of a full-strength syrup in order to obtain a syrup which is 15% of full strength?

6. The College Pharmacy has on hand a 10% and a 15% solution of argyrol. How should these be mixed in order to obtain 15 ounces of a 12% solution?

7. Find the interest on \$743 at 8% from April 12, 1961 to September 26, 1961. Use ordinary interest for exact time.

8. Solve for x: $2x + 17 = 33 - 2x$.

9. Solve for x: $7x - 15 = 4x + 18$.

10. Find the interest on \$1246 at 9% from June 24, 1962 to November 18, 1962. Use ordinary interest for exact time.

11. Divide 6.7342 by 87.6. Assume both are approximate numbers.

12. Divide 275.73 by 1.64. Assume both are approximate numbers.

13. Multiply 47.8×0.02693. Assume both are approximate numbers.

14. Multiply 69.472×39.8. Assume both are approximate numbers.

15. Add the approximate numbers $894.37 + 62.93 + 427 + 472.58 + 324.5$.

16. Add the approximate numbers $756.83 + 29.78 + 543 + 547.67 + 536.7$.

17. Subtract the approximate numbers $69.38 - 25.768$.

18. Subtract the approximate numbers $439.09 - 38.79$.

19. In the center of a circular pool in ancient Peking there stood a tall straight reed which extended two arms length above the level of the water. When a strong wind blew the reed, the tip touched the edge of the pool at the water level. If the radius of the pool was 8 arms' length, how deep was the pool?

20. Jim and Slim are carrying loads of 40 pounds and 50 pounds, respectively. How many pounds must be removed from Jim's load and added to Slim's load so that Jim will be carrying a load equal to $\frac{3}{4}$ of Slim's?

21. $I = E/R$ is Ohm's law in electricity. Solve this formula for R.

22. In problem 21, if $I = 5$ amperes, and $R = 20$ ohms, find E. The answer will be given in volts.

23. An automobile traveling at the speed of 55 miles per hour is traveling at how many feet per second?

24. How many gallons of water will it take to fill an aquarium whose inside dimensions are $18 \times 15 \times 12$ inches?

25. How many 8×8 inch asphalt tiles should Mr. Jerome buy to cover the floor of his 18 by 22 foot recreation room, assuming that an additional one-tenth will take care of waste?

26. If $1\frac{1}{4}$ inches on a map equals 50 miles, what distance will $4\frac{3}{8}$ inches represent?

27. If $4\frac{3}{8}$ inches on a map equals 245 miles, how many inches would there be between the map representations of two points that are actually 490 miles apart?

28. Find the proceeds from a loan of $1500 for a period of $2\frac{1}{2}$ years, if the charge is computed at 4% bank discount.

29. What is the annual simple interest rate on a loan of \$900 if three years' interest amounted to \$130.40?

30. Brown County Commissioner's Court passes a budget of \$4,040,064 to be raised by taxing real estate assessed at \$149,-632,000. What is to be the tax rate per \$100 valuation?

31. An electric dryer, rated at 4.2 kilowatts takes 30 minutes to dry a load of wash. What is the cost per load if the local utility company charges 4 cents per kilowatthour?

32. If 16.8 pounds of iron, when oxidized, yields 24.0 pounds of iron oxide, how much iron oxide can be made from a ton of iron?

33. If $C = \frac{5}{9}(F - 32)$, what is the Fahrenheit equivalent to 25° C?

34. If a gallon of paint covers 400 square feet, how many quart cans must be purchased to paint the ceiling and side walls of a room 18 by 24 feet, and 8 feet high, if windows and doors take up 20% of the wall area?

35. A suit, reduced 20% from its original price, is now on sale for \$67.75. What was the original price of the suit?

36. Change $\frac{3}{500}$ to a decimal.

37. Change $\frac{3}{4}\%$ to a decimal.

38. A metal washer has an outer diameter of 8.0 centimeters, a hole of diameter 2.0 centimeters, and a thickness of 2 millimeters. How many cubic centimeters of metal does it contain?

39. How many cubic feet of oil will a spherical oil tank 36 feet in diameter hold?

40. A 68 foot rope, when stretched from the top of a flagpole, touches the ground 22 feet from the base of the pole. How high is the pole?

41. Find the dimension of a square having the same area as a triangle whose base is 8 and altitude 64.

42. Find the number of minutes in y hours.

43. Find the number of weeks in d days.

44. If Susie is x years old now, how old will she be 12 years from now?

45. Solve $2x/3 = 54$ for x.

46. Solve $10.8 + 3x - 2 = 5.2 - 3$ for x.

47. If each of 21 long-playing records plays for 1 hour 32 minutes 14 seconds, how long will it take to hear them all?

48. The State Highway Commission condemned a strip of land 3286 feet long and 82 feet wide. How much will the owner receive if the property value is set at $645 an acre?

49. A spider is in the center of the floor of a building 30 yards long, 20 yards wide, and 12 feet high. How far will it walk by taking the shortest path to one of the upper corners of the ceiling?

50. How much lumber is required for the lateral surface of a cylindrical silo 28 feet high and 14 feet in diameter?

51. Hassocks are made in the form of right circular cylinders of diameter 26 inches and altitude 18 inches. Find the cost of construction if the leather covering costs $3.00 per square yard for the top and cylindrical surface, and $1.50 per square yard for the bottom? Waste should be figured at 12%. The filler and labor for each amounts to 76 cents.

52. Find the square root of 42.763.

53. Find the square root of 898.75.

54. Find the length of the diagonal of the rectangle whose length is 39 inches and whose width is 8.7 inches.

55. Find the length of the diagonal of the rectangle whose length is 562 centimeters and whose width is 425 centimeters.

56. A rectangular oil can has a square base $12\frac{1}{2}$ inches by $12\frac{1}{2}$ inches and is 14 inches deep. How many gallons does it hold?

57. Subtract 8 gallons 2 quarts 1 pint from 17 gallons.

58. Subtract 5 yards 2 feet 8 inches from 8 yards 6 inches.

59. An almanac says that $46\frac{1}{2}$ quarts of milk weigh 100 pounds. How much will a gallon of milk weigh?

60. Write any number of four digits in descending order. Reverse the order of the digits and subtract. Reverse the order of the digits in the remainder and add to the remainder. The sum will always be the same regardless of the number selected at the beginning.

61. Write the natural number 86 as a number with the base 2.

62. Write the natural number 124 as a number with the base 2.

63. 1011 is a number written in the binary system. Translate it into the decimal system.

64. 11100 is a number written in the binary system. Translate it into the decimal system.

ANSWERS TO ODD-NUMBERED PROBLEMS

Exercise 1, page 7

1. Fifty-three
3. Eight hundred thirty-four
5. Nine thousand, four hundred fifty-two
7. Twenty-four thousand, three hundred eighteen
9. Nine hundred thirty-two thousand, six hundred eighty-five
11. Two million, five hundred twenty-one thousand, four hundred thirty-seven
13. Twenty-one million, five hundred twenty-four thousand, seven hundred fifty-one
15. Seven hundred sixty-five million, seven hundred twenty-five thousand, eight hundred forty-three
17. Twenty-five trillion, seven hundred sixty-four billion, nine hundred fifty million, thirty-eight thousand, eight hundred forty-seven
19. Thirty-seven billion, six hundred eighty-three million, eight hundred twenty-one thousand, sixty-two

21. 837
23. 245,958
25. 93,248,005,035,427
27. 487,221,093,006
29. 1,001,001,001,100

Exercise 2, page 11

1. 26,933
3. 397; 346; 420; 414; 420; 507

5. $2201.65; $1903.71

7. 472; 473; 498; 425; $183.75; $207.03

9. 50,207,991
11. 8075
13. 85,378
15. 5,432,555
17. 82,101
19. 54,756,201,215
21. 105; 21
23. 656
25. $6\frac{1}{3}$ hours
27. $172.92
29. 260 pounds

Exercise 4, page 18

1. 16,013
3. 1,614,354
5. 88,055,215
7. 108,439,878
9. 8,967,476,625
11. 4,795,650,295
13. 48,396,645,360
15. 358,517,393,149

17. Thirty-nine million, eight hundred four thousand, three hundred seven; nine thousand seven

19. 70,786,759,284,331

21. (*a*) $4.50 (*b*) $6.00 (*c*) $10.15

23. $7.06
25. 4212 cubic feet
27. 50,400 pounds
29. 26,400 feet

Exercise 5, page 21

1. 57 r 36
3. 21 r 176
5. 9 r 346
7. 89 r 2442
9. 15 r 25,774
11. 3 r 153,693
13. 3 r 19,850
15. 1 r 1,699,667
17. 3 r 5,377,971
19. 369,975 r 522
21. 14
23. 17 miles per gallon
25. $350
27. 45
29. 1650

Exercise 6, page 23

1. VI
3. XXIII
5. XLVI
7. LXIV
9. LXXXII
11. CIII
13. DCXLIX
15. $\overline{\text{VII}}$DCLXXXIII
17. $\overline{\text{CDXXV}}$DCCLIII
19. 20
21. 37
23. 58
25. 73
27. 92
29. 228
31. 843
33. 6447
35. 352,437

Exercise 7, page 24

1. Eight thousand, three hundred fifty-four

3. Forty-two million, six hundred eighty-four thousand, three hundred forty-two

5. Thirty-six billion, seven hundred forty-three million, four hundred eighty-three thousand, seven hundred twenty-four

7. Five hundred forty-seven million, six hundred nineteen thousand, seven hundred eighty-three dollars

9. 301 eggs
11. 16,746,812,729,504
13. 17,091
17. 5,294,108,411
21. Grand Total = $9,125
23. $158.90

25. Nine hundred sixty-four billion, three hundred eighty-two million, four hundred sixty-three thousand, eight hundred thirty-nine

27. $11,043.75   29. 23 inches

Exercise 1, page 30

1. 6; 9; 75; 32.
3. $\frac{9}{24}$; $\frac{10}{24}$
5. $\frac{6}{24}$; $\frac{16}{24}$; $\frac{10}{24}$; $\frac{12}{24}$; $\frac{9}{24}$; $\frac{54}{24}$; $\frac{7}{24}$; $\frac{48}{24}$
7. 7 quarts   9. 28 ounces
11. $\frac{16}{40}$; $\frac{15}{40}$
13. $\frac{32}{48}$; $\frac{30}{48}$; $\frac{15}{48}$; $\frac{9}{48}$; $\frac{48}{48}$; $\frac{192}{48}$
15. 16 pints; 80 pints.
17. $\frac{3}{5}$ of 1 mile; $\frac{1}{35}$ of 1 mile.

Exercise 2, page 34

1. 1	3. 1	5. $\frac{2}{3}$	7. $1\frac{2}{5}$
9. $1\frac{5}{12}$	11. $\frac{16}{45}$	13. $1\frac{2}{3}$	15. $1\frac{11}{15}$
17. $-\frac{13}{80}$	19. $3\frac{67}{315}$	21. $\frac{2399}{2520}$	23. $\frac{49}{456}$
25. $\frac{3699}{38,038}$	27. $2\frac{319}{5040}$	29. $\frac{549}{1120}$	31. $\frac{11}{36}$
33. $\frac{67}{180}$	35. $\frac{3}{16}$	37. $\frac{67}{200}$	39. $\frac{11}{18}$; $\frac{7}{12}$; $\frac{5}{9}$; $\frac{1}{2}$

Exercise 3, page 36

1. $\frac{1}{2}$	3. $\frac{3}{20}$	5. $\frac{1}{24}$	7. $\frac{3}{7}$
9. $\frac{4}{45}$	11. $\frac{8}{91}$	13. $\frac{2}{63}$	15. $\frac{368}{4059}$
17. $\frac{1}{39}$	19. $\frac{13}{405}$	21. $4.62	25. 60 gallons

27. $342\frac{3}{8}$ square feet; $74\frac{1}{2}$ feet   29. 33 ounces
31. $\frac{7}{18}$ 33. First usher made best guess.

Exercise 4, page 39

1. $\frac{5}{3}$	3. $\frac{1}{2}$	5. $\frac{6}{5}$	7. $\frac{4}{9}$
9. $\frac{5}{8}$	11. 3	13. $\frac{49}{65}$	15. $\frac{5}{3}$
17. $\frac{8}{15}$	19. $\frac{7595}{6426}$	21. $\frac{85}{3}$	23. $\frac{1935}{352}$
25. $\frac{56}{87}$	27. $\frac{5}{2}$	29. $405\frac{1}{3}$ miles	31. 6
33. 78	35. $1\frac{3}{5}$ days	37. $\frac{8}{9}$ day	

Exercise 5, page 42

1. $8\frac{5}{8}$	3. $34\frac{109}{144}$	5. $31\frac{37}{56}$	7. $441\frac{11}{16}$
9. $2\frac{1}{24}$	11. $58\frac{57}{80}$	13. $607\frac{59}{72}$	15. $4\frac{45}{56}$
17. $4\frac{63}{80}$	19. $22\frac{83}{136}$	21. $42\frac{19}{68}$	23. $4\frac{7}{12}$
25. $11\frac{17}{126}$	27. $4\frac{16}{255}$	29. $\frac{193}{210}$	31. $12\frac{19}{60}$
33. $24\frac{151}{168}$	35. $\frac{4}{15}$	37. $\frac{100}{147}$	39. $105\frac{25}{56}$
41. $4\frac{19}{40}$ inches	43. $5\frac{1}{12}$ feet	45. $37\frac{7}{10}$ pounds	47. $23\frac{7}{8}$ yards
49. $20\frac{14}{15}$			

Exercise 6, page 46

1. $2\frac{11}{12}$
3. 12
5. $121\frac{22}{35}$
7. $7658\frac{26}{35}$
9. $4\frac{59}{64}$
11. 13
13. 2945
15. $236\frac{24}{35}$
17. $62\frac{718084}{912607}$
19. $23658\frac{146}{14763}$
21. $335\frac{15}{16}$ pounds
23. $2\frac{7}{24}$ miles; $2\frac{17}{24}$ miles

25. $10\frac{1}{2}$ cups flour, 14 teaspoons baking powder, $2\frac{5}{8}$ teaspoons salt, $8\frac{3}{4}$ tablespoons of sugar, $4\frac{3}{8}$ cups of milk, and $2\frac{1}{3}$ cups shortening.

27. $5\frac{5}{32}$ cubic yards or 6 cubic yards sand $9\frac{9}{32}$ barrels or 10 barrels lime

29. $449\frac{9}{32}$ bushels or 450 bushels

31. 20 days

Exercise 7, page 48

1. $1\frac{1}{5}$
3. $8\frac{5}{11}$
5. $2\frac{1}{2}$
7. $\frac{4706}{905}$
9. $6\frac{1}{3}$
11. $2\frac{635}{762}$
13. $1\frac{7}{13}$
15. $\frac{2}{5}$
17. $78\frac{1}{8}$
19. $\frac{28721}{38160}$
21. $\frac{5}{14}$
23. $1\frac{1}{20}$
25. $1\frac{1}{5}$
27. $11\frac{1}{2}$ inches
29. 7
31. 32 feet $\times$ 17 feet
33. 33
35. $4\frac{2}{3}$ feet

Exercise 8, page 50

1. $2\frac{172}{495}$
3. $\frac{2}{95}$
5. $\frac{4}{25}$
7. $\frac{4}{3}$
9. $\frac{5}{6}$
11. $143\frac{59}{228}$
13. $73\frac{99}{112}$
15. $23\frac{1}{3}$
17. $204{,}402\frac{89}{128}$
19. 25
21. 25
23. 240 pounds
25. $312\frac{1}{2}$ feet
27. \$3.47
29. 10 feet by 13 feet
31. $3\frac{3}{4}$ hours

33. Place two men in a group and ask one of them to hold a dollar bill. Give the third man a dollar, the fourth man a dollar, the fifth man a dollar, the sixth man a dollar, and the seventh man a dollar. There is now one dollar remaining. Go back to the first two men, and give the remaining dollar to the one who is not holding a dollar bill.

35. 270
37. $30\frac{15}{56}$ pounds
39. $\frac{4}{7}$

Exercise 1, page 59

1. 44,477.7554
3. 76370.8096
5. 4546.889
7. 6292.1736

9. Five hundred forty-seven and sixty-two hundredths.

11. Nine thousand, seven hundred sixty-three and seven hundred seventy-four thousandths.

13. Twelve thousand, five hundred eighty-seven and six thousand, seven hundred ninety-four ten thousandths.

15. Six hundred seventy-three thousand, five hundred four and eight thousand seventy-three ten thousandths.

17. Five million, eight hundred seven thousand, six hundred sixty-nine and seventy-five thousand nine hundred thirty-four hundred thousandths.

19. 8624.75
21. 65,759.483
23. 675,243.8726
25. 3,562,763.48965
27. 6028.56
29. 523,314.58284
31. $111.69
33. $6367.98
35. June 29
37. 847.088
39. 1436.947
41. 545.698
43. 0.8; 0.9; 0.875; 0.5625; 0.2
45. 1.5; 1.125; 4.75; 5.2; 3.125
47. $\frac{9}{25}; \frac{17}{40}; \frac{5}{8}; \frac{24}{25}; \frac{1}{16}$
49. $\frac{6}{5}$; $\frac{907}{20}$; $16\frac{5}{8}$; $21\frac{3}{8}$; $140\frac{1}{4}$

Exercise 2, page 63

1. 1063.044
3. 51016.2622
5. 697,086.2512
7. 2,231,432.38896
9. 87,770,463.664653

17. Two million, two hundred thirty-one thousand, four hundred thirty-two and thirty-eight thousand eight hundred ninety-six hundred thousandths.

19. Eighty-seven thousand, three hundred forty-eight and six hundred fifty-seven thousandths; one thousand four and eight hundred twenty-nine thousandths.

21. $225,841,600
23. $2904.00
25. 2046.22 feet
27. $17.04
29. $7.08

Exercise 3, page 66

1. 65.38
3. 579.68
5. 804.695
7. 4007.896
9. 1.70
11. 69.57
13. 8.87
15. 0.13
17. 306.53
19. 1.03
21. $19.67
23. $67.68
25. 4758 yards
27. $17.35
29. 7 quarts

31. Place 3 plums in one cup and 7 in another, and then place one of these in the third cup.

Exercise 1, page 75

1. 43,560 square feet
3. 283 inches
5. 138 pints
7. 246 ounces
9. 3572 rods
11. 760 quarts
13. 92 cups
15. 304,920 square feet
17. 2604 square yards
19. 16 pounds and 1 ounce
21. 34 feet and 8 inches
23. 18.375 gallons
25. 271 quarts
27. 2534 cubic yards
29. 142 rods, 5 feet
31. 7 bushels, 1 peck, 6 quarts

33. 4 tons, 764 pounds
35. 276 quarts
37. 355 pounds, 4 ounces
39. 191 gallons, 2 quarts
41. 172 hours, 12 minutes, 3 seconds
43. 33 pounds, 9 ounces
45. 25 feet, 11 inches
47. 4 hours, 33 minutes
49. 47 gallons, 1 quart, 1 pint
51. 246 feet
53. 2285 pounds, 12 ounces
55. 2706 hours, 8 minutes
57. 6394 square feet, 23 square inches
59. 170,796 square feet, 89 square inches
61. 26 pounds, 9 ounces
63. 17 hours, $35\frac{1}{4}$ minutes
65. $42\frac{9}{25}$
67. $8\frac{12}{241}$
69. $2.99
71. $92.40
73. 6 pounds, $3\frac{5}{8}$ ounces
75. 1600 fuses
77. 30 feet, 8 inches
79. 21 revolutions per second
81. $57
83. 125 gallons
85. 1920 revolutions
87. 864,000 revolutions
89. 390 revolutions
91. 672 squares of tile

Exercise 2, page 81

1. 1000 millimeters
3. 30 centimeters
5. 5 grams
7. 100,000 centigrams
9. 17,500 centimeters
11. 50,000 milliliters
13. 23 kilometers, 254 meters, 69 centimeters
15. 5 meters, 3 decimeters
17. 0.6 kilogram
19. 4000 centigrams
21. 4750 grams
23. 0.356 kilometers
25. 2500 centiliters
27. meter
29. kilometer
31. 123.342 kilometers
33. 54.38 square centimeters
35. 1380 kilograms
37. 8 centimeters
39. 4500 square centimeters

Exercise 3, page 86

1. ——
700,000
168,000,000

26,000
0.0005
0.0000000000163

6,300,000,000
——
0.032

1,860,000,000,000
980,000,000
0.0000000000000000000000164

3. 29,980,000,000; 0.00000000000000000000000006547; 0.000000000477; 109737; 0.00000000000000000000000165

Exercise 4, page 88

1. 110
3. 10111
5. 101110
7. 1000000
9. 1010010
11. 1100111
13. 1010001001
15. 2
17. 5
19. 8
21. 13
23. 15
25. 26
27. 292

Exercise 5, page 90

1. 590.6 inches
3. 91.44 meters
5. 15200 gallons per hour
7. 53.0 grams per second
9. 12.0 miles
11. 2.54 centimeters
13. 10.8 square feet
15. 10.7 meters
17. 22,500 meters
19. 143 feet
21. 24.7 feet
23. 0.369 kilogram
25. 0.709 kilogram
27. 172.0 pounds
29. 2808 cubic inches
31. 2.53 pounds
33. 0.819 pounds
35. 154.4 meters
37. 84.51 miles
39. 11.4 kilograms

Exercise 6, page 91

1. 132.42
3. 156 times
5. 0.768
7. $1.68
9. $178\frac{23}{27}$

11. Seven hundred thirty-two billion, five hundred sixty-four million, eight hundred fifty-nine thousand, six hundred eight

13. 6.37×10^7
15. 37,000,000,000
17. 1000011110
19. 512
21. 63.3
23. 26
25. 53.51
27. 90°
29. 1400 cubic feet
31. 0.843
33. 20 miles
35. 1100 square inches
37. $\frac{5}{7}$
39. $\frac{2}{7}$
41. 225
43. 168
45. $12
47. 0.433
49. 1.47; 0.08; 9.63
51. 250
53. MCMXLI
55. 1600
57. 4.15×10^5
59. 1,990,000,000,000,000,000,000,000,-000,000,000

Exercise 1, page 98

1. 0.02
3. 0.055
5. 0.75
7. 1.25
9. 4.50
11. 50.25
13. 0.5265
15. 3.845
17. 60.2775
19. 25.47125
21. 0.18
23. 0.15

Exercise 2, page 99

1. 5%
3. 7.25%
5. 9¾%
7. 83.92%
9. 247.3%
11. 6792%
13. 75323½%
15. 4.758%
17. 6433¼%
19. 47325%
21. 29%
23. 652.7%

Exercise 3, page 100

1. $\frac{7}{100}$ 3. $\frac{1}{4}$ 5. $\frac{5}{4}$
7. $\frac{13}{400}$ 9. $\frac{261}{400}$ 11. $5\frac{51}{200}$
13. $52\frac{11}{20}$ 15. $\frac{7}{3}$ 17. $\frac{313}{40,000}$
19. $7\frac{1153}{2000}$ 21. $\frac{2}{5}$
23. $\frac{3}{20}$, $\frac{3}{20}$, $\frac{3}{20}$

Exercise 4, page 101

1. 60% 3. $62\frac{1}{2}\%$ 5. 425%
7. 600% 9. 162.5% 11. 75%
13. 500% 15. 30,000% 17. 1525%
19. 89.5%
21. 58%; $\frac{3}{5}$; $0.6\frac{3}{5}$; $\frac{18}{23}$ 23. $\frac{3}{8}$; $0.4\frac{3}{4}$; $62\frac{1}{2}\%$; $\frac{3}{4}$

25. Three; three hundred per cent, three hundred-hundredths; eight; eight hundred per cent; one hundred fifty-fiftieths; 3; 300%; $\frac{300}{100}$; $\frac{150}{50}$; 8; 800%.

27. $\frac{1}{4}$; 25%

Exercise 5, page 103

1. 13.28 3. 35.75 5. 109.86
7. 4% 9. 66.6% 11. 7.76%
13. 200 15. 191.67 17. 85.60
19. 274.29 21. 8.54 23. 52.70%
25. 232.20% 27. 269.20% 29. 1663.60%
31. 1099.98 33. 1244.88 35. 1517.86
37. 19.20 39. 175.13 41. 481 pounds
43. $33\frac{1}{3}\%$ 45. 12.36% 47. $225,000
49. 33.91%; $529.67 51. $18.38

53. cement 20%; sand 40%; gravel 40%
55. 55,000 pounds
57. 2100 ounces gold; 1225 ounces silver; 175 ounces copper
59. 0.3%
61. 778.72 pounds
63. 5636.36 pounds lynite
65. 91.2%

Exercise 6, page 108

1. $2.47 3. 23%

5. 50% profit on cost; $33\frac{1}{3}\%$ profit on selling price

7. $4133.33 9. 314.96
11. $122.18 13. $4.50
15. $2936 17. $2.40; 15.74%; 84.26%

19. $695; 134.95%
21. $115.36
23. $33.33
25. $5630.53
27. It makes no difference.
29. $45

Exercise 1, page 118

1. pound
3. 10 quarts
5. 100 feet
7. 0.001 foot
9. 0.1 mile
11. dollar
13. dollar
15. 0.01 inch
17. 0.001 gallon
19. ¼ foot
21. 4
23. 5
25. 6
27. 6
29. 1
31. 1
33. 7
35. 3
37. 7
39. 6
41. 5433
43. 392.6
45. 65.04
47. 3595.6
49. 25,136
51. 91.544
53. 64.8
55. 784.9
57. 6849.0
59. 127.87
61. 8579.01
63. 785,884.07

Exercise 2, page 120

1. 100,452.30
3. 10,283.77

5. Six hundred fourteen and thirty-eight-hundredths; fifty-nine and four thousand seven hundred eighty-six-ten thousandths; six hundred fourteen-thousands; seven and five thousand three hundred twenty-eight-ten thousandths; nine thousand five hundred sixty-two and nine thousand nine hundred ninety-nine-ten thousandths; thirty-eight and seventy-six thousand four hundred thirty-five-hundred thousandths; ten thousand two hundred eighty-three and seventy-seven-hundredths.

7. 413.14
9. 5123.095
11. 97782.3
13. 119 miles
15. 2715.1 miles
17. 78 gallons
19. 87.3 hours

Exercise 3, page 126

1. 5700
3. 45,600
5. 86,638,000
7. 1437
9. 29375
11. 41,987,900

13. Five thousand six hundred forty-three and sixty-seven-hundredths; seven thousand four hundred thirty-nine and eighty-two-hundredths; forty-one million nine hundred eighty-seven thousand nine hundred.

15. 391,000
17. 215,680,000
19. 52,300,000,000,000
21. 2.44
23. 597.7
25. 10.193
27. 9.129
29. 16.269
31. 629

33. Four thousand seven hundred fifty-three; two million, nine hundred eighty-nine thousand, six hundred thirty-seven; six hundred twenty-nine.

35. 15.795
37. 12.2920

39. Sixteen and five thousand seven hundred ninety-three-ten thousandths; two hundred three and seven thousand nine hundred twenty-one-ten thousandths: twelve and two thousand nine hundred twenty-ten thousandths.

41. 1540 square inches, 1548 square inches, 1540 square inches

43. 356,000 square feet
45. 362 square feet
47. 146 square inches
49. 0.72
51. 83.0 kilograms
53. 38.9%
55. 26 square yards
57. 450.2 feet
59. 60 miles

Exercise 1, page 133

1. Four x square; 4; 2.
3. Fifteen x cube z to the fourth; 15; 3; 4.
5. Thirty-five a to the fourth b to the fifth c to the sixth; 35; 4; 5; 6.
7. Three fourths x square y cube; $\frac{3}{4}$; 2; 3.
9. Fourteen x cube y square z to the fourth; 14; 3; 2; 4.

11. $4x^2y$
13. a^5
15. $42x^3y^2$
17. $184x^6y^3$
19. $42c^6d^2$
21. 4
23. 8
25. 8
27. 4
29. 44
31. 3
33. 72
35. 8
37. 216
39. $4\frac{1}{2}$

Exercise 2, page 136

1. −25
3. 18
5. −18
7. $208\frac{1}{4}$
9. $-241\frac{3}{16}$
11. 11
13. −18
15. −33
17. $74\frac{11}{12}$
19. −332.7
21. 30
23. 36
25. −92
27. −34.884
29. $22{,}292\frac{19}{32}$
31. 4
33. −9
35. 6
37. −0.2
39. 0.02

Exercise 3, page 140

1. $x = 4$
3. $x = -5$
5. $x = 6$
7. $x = 7\frac{1}{2}$
9. $x = 15$
11. $x = 7\frac{3}{4}$
13. $x = 38$
15. $x = 15.1$
17. $x = 5$
19. $x = 8$
21. $x = 11\frac{2}{3}$
23. $x = 4\frac{1}{2}$
25. $x = 40$
27. $x = \frac{17}{48}$
29. $x = 4\frac{1}{4}$
31. 70; 77
33. 46; 48; 50
35. 30; 65

37. 12 = son's age, 9 = daughter's age, 45 = man's age

39. \$5000; \$15,000
41. 8
43. 27; 28; 29
45. 39

Exercise 4, page 146

1. 79 days
3. 155 days
5. 301 days
7. 267 days
9. 126 days
11. 246 days
13. 253 days
15. 308 days
17. $21.58
19. $4.74
21. $145.08
23. $210
25. 123 days
27. 3.72%
29. $1600
31. $4455.45
33. $1752; $1800
35. $632.38

Exercise 5, page 150

1. 72.7 feet
3. 95.2 feet
5. 150.3 inches
7. $p = 4s$
9. 294 feet
11. 66.76 inches
13. 16.9 inches
15. 20 feet by 40 feet
17. 49 feet, 49 feet, 41 feet
19. 12 small square; 36 larger square

Exercise 6, page 153

1. 120 square feet
3. 4600 square feet
5. 2600 square inches
7. 1600 square inches
9. 640 acres
11. 61
13. 20 bundles
15. 120 square feet
17. 92.1 feet
19. 38 cents

Exercise 7, page 155

1. 50
3. 8900 square feet
5. 38 square centimeters
7. 2,160,000 square meters
9. 11,000 square inches
13. 1300 square inches
15. 3.81 feet

Exercise 8, page 160

1. 7.0
3. 66.00
5. 13.100
7. 4.17000
9. 11.60
11. 77.481
13. 88.840
15. 11.1652
17. 0.079
19. 0.1300
21. 17.0 feet
23. 54 feet
25. 36.2 feet
27. 21 feet
29. 9 feet

Exercise 9, page 162

1. 100 square inches
3. 1990 square meters
5. 13,400 square feet
7. 5500 square inches
9. 12,100 square kilometers
11. 300
13. 2700 square inches
15. 139,000 square kilometers
17. 580 square feet
19. 170 square inches
21. $\pi(r_1^2 - r_2^2)$
23. $\sqrt{\frac{A}{\pi}}$
25. 6.8 feet

Exercise 10, page 164

1. $\frac{101}{51}$
3. $\frac{1}{36}$
5. $\frac{4}{9}$
7. \$4.08; \$6.12
9. $\frac{1}{2}$
11. $\frac{16}{13}$
13. 500 miles
15. 15 cubic yards
17. 16 pounds
19. \$3.60
21. \$4.30
23. 7511 pounds
25. \$6000; \$8000; \$10,000

Exercise 1, page 169

1. 60 cubic inches
3. 8 inches
5. 730 bushels
7. 10 tons
9. 13,000 bricks
11. 20 cubic feet
13. 363 square yards
15. 720 square feet
17. 416 square feet
19. 190 square feet
21. 60 square feet
23. 580 square inches
25. 510 cubic inches

Exercise 2, page 172

1. 2800 cubic inches
3. $2\pi rh + 2\pi r^2$
5. 1620 square feet
7. 410 square centimeters
9. 2700 pounds
11. 1200 square feet
13. 9 gallons
15. 150 gallons

Exercise 3, page 174

1. 1740 cubic inches
3. 3.7 cubic yards
5. $h = \frac{3v}{\pi r^2}$
7. 4230 square inches
9. 153 square feet
11. 13.7 centimeters
13. 29.1 inches
15. 1140 cubic feet

Exercise 4, page 176

1. 3380 square inches
3. 18,470 cubic inches
5. 2400 cubic feet
7. 870 square feet
9. 300 square inches
11. 360 square inches
13. 150 squares
15. Multiplies the volume by 64
17. 800 feet over
19. 500 square inches

Exercise 5, page 177

1. 56 feet
3. 0.299
5. $\frac{3}{17}$ quart
7. \$27.58
9. 11
11. 0.0769
13. 1.29
15. 2181
17. 43.61
19. 15 arms length
21. $R = E/I$
23. 81 feet per second
25. 1000
27. $8\frac{3}{4}$ inches
29. 4.8%
31. 8.4 cents
33. 77°
35. \$84.69
37. 0.0075
39. 24,000 cubic feet

41. 16×16
43. $\frac{d}{7}$
45. 81
47. 32 hours, 16 minutes, 54 seconds
49. 27 feet
51. $6.64
53. 29.979
55. 705 centimeters
57. 8 gallons, 1 quart, 1 pint
59. 8.6 pounds
61. 1010110
63. 11

INDEX

Absolute values, 134
Acre, 73, 74
Addends, 8
Addition, 8
Algebra, word problems in, 140
Approximate numbers, 113, 114
  addition and subtraction of, 119
  division of, 124
  multiplication of, 122
    and division of, 122
Approximate time, 145
Area formulas for circle and ellipse, 161
Area formulas for the rectangle, parallelogram, and triangle, 151
Area formula for the trapezoid, 154
Area of lateral surface of a regular pyramid, 169
Areas and volumes of elementary solids, 167
Arithmetic in the business world, 106

Bale, 74
Bank discount, 144
Barrel, 73
Base, find the, 102
Base ten, 6
Bell, E. T., 3
Binary system, 87
Binomial, 132
Bundle, 74
Bushel, 73
Business fractions, 100

Carat, 74
Casting out nines, 14
Centigram, 80
Century, 74
Chain, 74
Checking by casting out nines, 14
Circle, 161
Circumference, 148
Commercial year, 74
Common Year, 74
Cone, 173
  lateral area, 173
  volume, 174
Conversion of units, 89
Cord, 74
Cubic foot, 73, 74
Cubic inches, 73
Cubic meter, 89
Cubic yard, 73, 89
Cup, 73

Cylinder, 171
  right circular, 171
  right circular, lateral area, 172
  right circular, lateral surface, 172
  right circular, volume, 171

Dantzig, Tobias, 3
Day, 74
Decade, 74
Decigram, 80
Decimal fractions, adding and subtracting, 57
  dividing, 64
  multiplying, 62
  reduction to a per cent, 98
Decimal places, 56
Decimal point, 55
Decimals, 55
Decimal system, 5, 55, 87
Decimeter, 80
Dekagram, 80
Dekameter, 80
Denominator, 29
  lowest common, 31
Difference, 9
Divide powers of ten, 83
Dividend, 19
Division, checking by casting out nines, 21
  definition, 19
  process of measuring, 20
  process of partitioning, 20
  standard check, 21
Divisor, 19
Dollar markup, 107
Dram, 73

Electronic digital computers, 87
Elementary algebra, 131
Ellipse, 162
  area of, 162
  major axis of, 162
  minor axis of, 162
  semi-major axis of, 162
  semi-minor axis of, 162
Equations, basic rule in the handling of, 138
  checking the solution of, 139

Exact numbers, 113
Exact time, 145
Excess of a number in casting out nines, 14
Exponent, 82, 133
Exponents and scientific notation, 82

Factor, 32, 132
  numerical, 132
  prime, 32
Fluid dram, 74
Fluid ounce, 74
Foot, 73
Formula, defined, 143
Formulas from commercial algebra, 142
  perimeter and circumference, 148
Fractions, 29
  changed to higher terms, 30
  common, 29
  equivalent, 29
  fundamental principle of, 30
  improper, 29
  inverting the divisor of, 38
  measurement, 38
  reduced to lower terms, 30
  terms of, 29
Furlong, 74

Gallon, 73, 74
Gram, 80
Gross margin, 106
Gross profit, 106

Hand, 74
Hectogram, 80
Hectometer, 80
Hogben, Lancelot, 1
Hogshead, 73
Hour, 74
Hundredweight, 73
Hypotenuse, 159

Improper fractions, adding and subtracting, 40
  dividing, 47
  multiplying, 45
Inch, 89

Integers, 5
Interest, 142
  charged in advance, 143

Kasner, E., 3
Kilogram, 80, 89
Kilometer, 80
Knot, 74

Leap year, 74
Legs, 159
Link, 74
Liter, 89
Literal factors, 132
Long ton, 73
Loss, 106

Markup, 106
Measurements and approximate numbers, 113
Meter, 79, 89
Metric system of weights and measures, 79
Mile, 73, 74
Minuend, 9
Minute, 74
Mixed numbers, adding and subtracting, 40
  dividing, 47
  multiplying, 45
Monomials, 132
Multinomial, 132
Multiplicand, 17
Multiplication, checking by casting out nines, 17
  definition, 16
Multiplier, 17
Multiply powers of ten, 83

Natural numbers, 5
Negative exponents, 85
Negative numbers, 134
Net profit, 106
Newman, James R., 3
No ratio, 164
Numerator, 29

Ordinary and exact interest, 145
Ounce, 73

Parallelogram, 151
  area of, 152
Peck, 73
Per cent, 97
Percentage, 97, 98, 102
  base, 102
  finding, 102
  rate, 102
  three cases of, 102
Perimeter, 148
Pi, 149
Pint, 73, 74
Polygon, 168
  regular, 168
Pound, 73, 89
Product, 17
Profit on cost, 107
Proper fractions, adding and subtracting, 29
  dividing, 37
  multiplying, 35
Proportion, 164
Pyramid, 168
  altitude, 168
  lateral surface, 169
  regular, 168
  slant height, 168
  vertex, 168
  volume, 169
Pythagorean theorem and some of its applications, 159

Quart, 73, 89
Quire, 74
Quotient, 19

Rate, 102
Ratio, 163
Ratio and proportion, 163
Ream, 74
Rectangle, 149
  area of, 151
Rectangular solid, 167
Rectangular solid and pyramid, 167
Reduction of a common fraction to a per cent, 101

Reduction of a per cent to a common fraction, 99
Remainder, 9
Remainder in casting out nines, 14
Rent, 142
Representative of the sum in casting out nines, 15
Right triangle, 159
Rod, 73, 74
Roman notation for numbers, 22
Roman numerals, 5, 22
Roman symbols, 22
Rounding a number, 117
Rounding numbers, 117

Scientific notation, 83
Scruple, 73
Section, 74
Selling expense, 106
Signed numbers, adding and subtracting, 134
  dividing, 136
  multiplying, 135
Significant figures, 115
  zeros, 116
Single discount rate, 99
Solids, 167
Solving simple linear equations, 137
Sphere, 175
  surface area, 175
  volume, 175
Square, 149
Square chain, 74
Square foot, 73
Square meter, 89
Square mile, 73
Square rod, 73, 74
Square root, 156
Square roots of approximate numbers, 158
Square yard, 73, 89
Subtraction, 9
  addition check, 10
  decomposition method, 9
  equal additions method, 10
Subtrahend, 9

Terms, 132
Theorem of Pythagoras, 159
Ton, 73
Township, 74
Transcendental number, 149
Triangle, 148
  vertex, 168
Trinomial, 132

Units of measurement, 114

Week, 74
Weights and measures, national system of, 71
Whole numbers, adding and subtracting, 7
  dividing, 19
  multiplying, 5, 16
  reading and writing, 6

Yard, 73
Year, 74

Zeros may or may not be significant, 116
  not significant, 116